Dear Ryan,

Congratulations on
your graduation from
school for the show

Love
Uncle Jean &
Aunt [...]
x

Rand McNally

The Comprehensive World Atlas

Longmeadow Press

Contents

The Comprehensive World Atlas

Copyright © 1988 by Rand McNally & Company
Pages iii, iv, and 1 to 224 from *Concise World Atlas*,
Copyright © 1987 by Rand McNally & Company.
Pages v-xv from *Illustrated Atlas of the World*.
Copyright © 1985 by Rand McNally & Company.
Page xvi from *Cosmopolitan World Atlas*,
Copyright © 1987 by Rand McNally & Company.

Published by Longmeadow Press
201 High Ridge Road
Stamford, CT 06304

Printed in the United States of America
ISBN 0-681-40707-7

0 9 8 7 6 5 4 3 2 1

Using the Atlas

Sequence of the Maps

The world is made up of seven major land-masses: the continents of Europe, Asia, Africa, Australia, South America, North America, and Antarctica (figure 5). To allow for the inclusion of detail, each continent is broken down into a series of maps, and this grouping is arranged so that as consecutive pages are turned, a continuous and successive part of the continent is shown. Larger-scale maps are used for regions of greater detail (having many cities, for example) or for areas of global significance.

The continental sequence of the maps is as follows: Europe (traditionally first in atlases), Asia (connected to Europe and forming the Eurasian landmass), Africa, Australia and Oceania, South America, and North America.

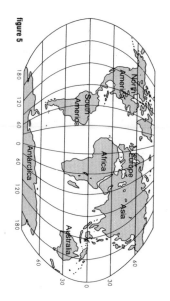

figure 5

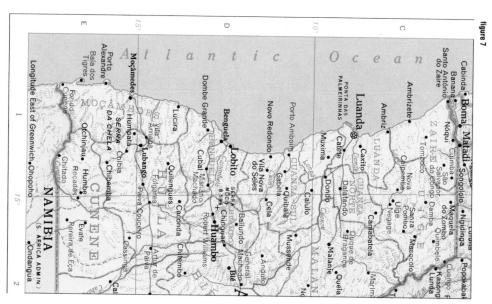

figure 7

Benevento, Italy, U.S.	E2 87
Benevolence, Ga., U.S.	E2 87
Benewah, co., Id., U.S.	B2 89
Benezett, Pa., U.S.	D5 115
Benfeld, Fr.	A3 20
Bengal, OK., U.S.	D8 113
Bengal, hist reg, Asia	F8 36
Bengal, Bay of, b., Asia	D7 36
Ben Gardane, Tun.	B8 31
Bengbu, China.	C4 43
Benghazi (Banghāzī), Libya	E8 31
Bengkalis, Indon.	E2 34
Bengkalis, i., Indon.	L5 35
Bengkulu, Indon.	F2 34
Bengo, dept., Ang.	C1 48
Bengo, stm., Ang.	D1 48
Benguela, dept., Ang.	H3 75
Benguela, Ang.	D1 48
Benguela, Sk., Can.	C1 48
Benham, Ky., U.S.	D7 94
Ben Hill, co., Ga., U.S.	E3 87
Beni, Zaire	D7 45
Beni, Nig.	B2 55
Berati, Alb.	A4 48
Berach, stm., India	D7 45
Berau, F.R.Ger.	B2 55
Berau, Bay, b., Indon.	C4 44
Berbera, Som.	
Berberati, Cen. Afr. Rep.	
Berbice, stm., Guy.	
Berceto, Italy	
Bercher, Switz.	
Berchogur, Sov. Un.	
Berchtesgaden, F.R.Ger.	
Berck, Fr.	
Berclair, Tx., U.S.	
Berdichev, Sov. Un.	
Berdsk, Sov. Un.	
Berdyansk, Sov. Un.	
Berea, Ky., U.S.	

figure 6

2. Turn to the map of Central Africa on page 48. Note that the letters A through E and the numbers 1 through 7 appear in the margins of the maps.

3. To find Benguela on the map, place your left index finger on D and your right index finger on 1. Move your left finger across the map and your right finger into the map. Your fingers will meet in the area in which Benguela is located (figure 7).

Getting the Information

An atlas can be used for many purposes, from planning a trip to finding hot spots in the news and supplementing world knowledge. But to realize the full potential of an atlas, the user must be able to:

1. Find places on the maps
2. Measure distances
3. Determine directions
4. Understand map symbols

Finding Places

One of the most common and important tasks facilitated by an atlas is finding the *location* of a place in the world. A river's name in a book, a city mentioned in the news, or a vacation spot may prompt your need to know where the place is located. The illustrations and text below explain how to find Benguela, Angola.

1. Look up the place-name in the index at the back of the atlas. Benguela, Angola, can be found on the map on page 48, and it can be located on the map by the letter-number key *D1* (figure 6).

Measuring Distances

In planning trips, determining the distance between two places is essential, and an atlas can help in travel preparation. For instance, to determine the approximate distance between Paris and Rouen, France, follow these three steps:

1. Lay a slip of paper on the map on page 16 so that its edge touches the two cities. Adjust the paper so one corner touches Rouen. Mark the paper directly at the spot where Paris is located (figure 8).

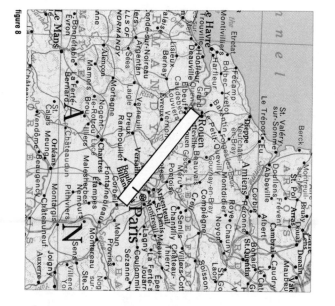

figure 8

2. Place the paper along the scale of statute miles beneath the map. Position the corner at 0 and line up the edge of the paper along the scale. The pencil mark on the paper indicates Rouen is between 50 and 75 miles from Paris (figure 9).

3. To find the exact distance, move the paper to the left so that the pencil mark is at 50 on the scale. The corner of the paper stands in the fourth 5-mile unit on the scale. This means that the two towns are 50 miles plus 15 miles plus 2 miles, or 67 miles, apart (figure 10).

Statute Miles 25 0 25 50 75

figure 9

Statute Miles 25 0 25 50 75

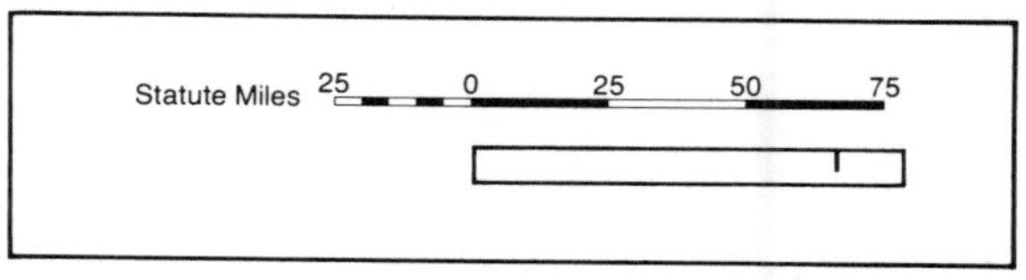

figure 10

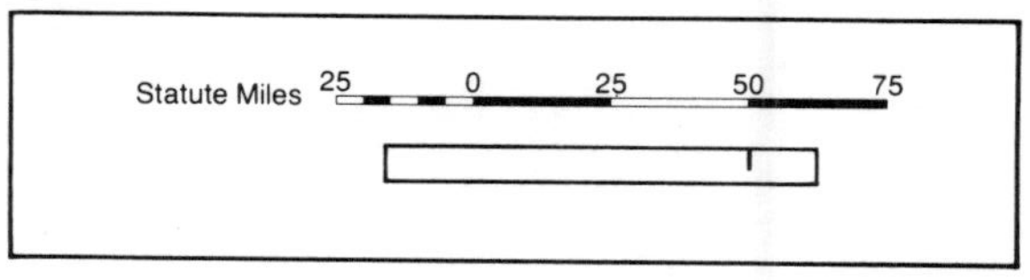

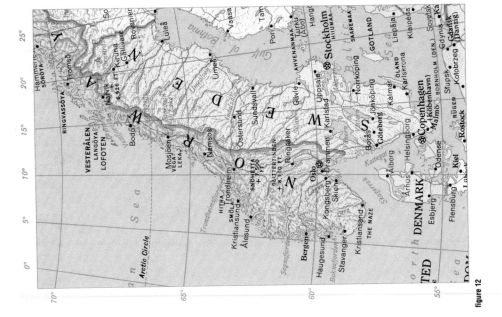

figure 12

The scale relationship of the map to the earth may also be expressed as a ratio, for example, 1:1,000,000 (one to one million). The map unit in the ratio is always given as one, and the number of similar units the map unit represents on the earth's surface is written after the colon. Thus for a 1:1,000,000 map, 1 inch on the map represents 1,000,000 inches on the earth's surface. In order to determine how many miles on the earth 1 inch on the map represents, divide 63,360 (the number of inches in one mile) into 1,000,000. This results in the written scale for a 1:1,000,000 map being stated as, 1 inch (on the map) = 16 miles (on the earth).

Determining Directions

Most of the maps in the atlas are drawn so that when oriented for normal reading north is at the top of the map, south is at the bottom, west is at the left, and east is at the right. Most maps have a series of lines drawn across them — the lines of latitude and longitude. Lines of latitude, or parallels of latitude, are drawn east and west. Lines of longitude, or meridians of longitude, are drawn north and south (figure 11).

Parallels and meridians appear as either curved or straight lines. For example, in the section of the map of Europe in figure 12, the parallels of latitude appear as curved lines. The meridians of longitude are straight lines that come together toward the top of the map.

Latitude and longitude lines help locate places on maps. Parallels of latitude are numbered in degrees north and south of the *Equator.* Meridians of longitude are numbered in degrees east and west of a line called the *Prime Meridian,* running through Greenwich, England, near London. Any place on earth can be located by the latitude and longitude lines running through it.

To determine directions or locations on maps, you must use the parallels and meridians. For example, suppose you want to know which city is farther north, Bergen, Norway, or Stockholm, Sweden. The map in figure 12 shows that Stockholm is south of the 60° parallel of latitude and Bergen is north of it. This means that Bergen is farther north than Stockholm. By looking at the meridians of longitude, you can determine which city is farther east. Bergen is approximately 5° east of the 0° meridian (Prime Meridian), and Stockholm is almost 20° east of it. This means that Stockholm is farther east than Bergen.

Understanding Map Symbols

In a very real sense, the whole map is a symbol, representing the world or a part of it. It is a reduced representation of the earth; each of the world's features — cities, rivers, etc. — is represented on the map by a symbol. Map symbols may take the form of points, such as dots or stars (often used for cities, capital cities, or points of interest), or lines (roads, rivers, railroads). Symbols may also occupy an area, showing extent of coverage (states, forests, deserts). They seldom look like the feature they represent and therefore must be identified and interpreted. For instance, the maps in this atlas show and differentiate political units (countries, states) with color. The political units are further defined by a heavy line depicting their boundaries. Neither the colors nor the boundary lines are actually found on the surface of the earth, but because countries and states are such important political components of the world, strong symbols are used to represent them.

The legend on page 1 identifies the symbols used in this atlas.

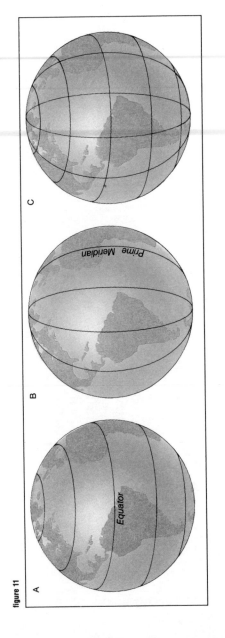

figure 11

A   B   C

Equator   Prime Meridian

The Earth and The Universe

Stars vary enormously in size, temperature and luminosity. The largest, so-called red giants like Antares (1)—the biggest yet known—or Aldebaran (2), are nearing the end of their lives: dwindling nuclear "fuel" causes their expand. Rigel (3) is many times brighter than our Sun (4)—a middle-aged star—but both are so-called main-sequence stars. Epsilon Eridani (5) is rather like the Sun. Wolf 359 (6) is a red dwarf.

The Big Bang theory above, of the origin of the universe envisages all matter originating from one point in time and space — a point of infinite density. In the intensely hot Big Bang all the material that goes to make up the planets, stars and galaxies that we see now began to expand outward in all directions. This expansion has been likened to someone blowing up a balloon on which spots have been painted. As the air fills and expands the balloon, the spots get farther away from each other. Likewise, clusters of galaxies that formed from the original superdense matter began, and continue, to move away from neighboring clusters.

These black holes are regions in which matter has become so concentrated that the force of gravity makes it impossible for anything—even light itself—to escape. As stars are pulled apart by gravitational forces, and their material forms into a swirling maelstrom from which huge explosions can occur. Collapse into black holes, accompanied by violent outbursts from the maelstrom, may be the ultimate fate of all matter in the universe. For our own Solar System, however, such a fate is far in the future: the Sun in its present form is believed to have enough "fuel" to keep it going for at least another 5,000 million years.

The evidence of just why these huge explosions occur is often hard to obtain, because the exploding galaxies may be so far away that light from them takes millions of years to reach telescopes on Earth. But it is becoming increasingly accepted by astronomers that such violent events may be associated with the presence of black holes at the centers of some galaxies.

Galaxies consist of star systems, dust clouds and gases formed from the hot material exploding outward from the original cosmic fireball. Our own Milky Way system, the band of light that stretches across the night sky, is typical of many galaxies, containing millions of stars slowly rotating around a central nucleus.

tionary concept of space-time. Einstein's theory of relativity describes the phenomenon, not in terms of galaxies moving through space in the expansion, but as being carried apart by the expansion of space-time itself. Space-time may be imagined as a rubber sheet speckled with paint blobs (galaxies), which move apart as the rubber sheet expands.

visioned in Einstein's revolutionary concept of space-time. the dimension of time, as envisioned in Einstein's revolutionary concept of space-time. sional matter and space but also includes not only all three-dimensional matter and space but also the dimension of time, as envisioned in Einstein's revolutionary concept of space-time.

Most astronomers believe that the universe began in a great explosion of matter and energy about 15,000 million years ago – the "Big Bang". This event was implied by Einstein's theory of general relativity, as well as by more recent astronomical observations and calculations. But the clinching evidence came in 1965, when two American radio astronomers discovered a faint, uniform, background radiation which permeated all space. This they identified as the remnants of the Big Bang.

The generally accepted explanation for the so-called "cosmic microwave" background, detected by American astronomers Arno Penzias and Robert Wilson, is indeed that it is the echo of the Big Bang itself, the radio noise left over from the fireball of creation. In recognition of their discovery, Penzias and Wilson shared a Nobel Prize in 1978.

The Big Bang has also been identified by astronomers in other ways. All the evidence shows that the universe is expanding, and its constituent parts—clusters of galaxies, each containing thousands of millions of stars like our Sun—are moving away from each other at great speeds. From this and other evidence scientists deduce that long ago the galaxies must have been closer together, in a superdense phase, and that at some time in the remote past all the material in the universe must have started spreading out from a single point. But this "single point" includes not only all three-dimen-

The Earth in The Solar System

Nuclear reactions in the Sun's core maintain a temperature of some 15,000,000°C and this heat prevents the star from shrinking. The surface temperature is comparatively much lower —a mere 6,000°C. Thermonuclear energy-generating processes cause the Sun to "lose" mass from the center at the rate of four million tonnes of hydrogen every second. This mass is turned into energy (heat), and each gram of matter "burnt" produces the heat equivalent of 100 trillion electric fires. The Sun's total mass is so great, however, that it contains enough matter to continue radiating at its present rate for several thousand million years before it runs out of "fuel."

The Sun's retinue

The Solar System emerged from a collapsing gas cloud. In addition to the Sun there are at least nine planets, their satellites, thousands of minor planets (asteroids), comets and meteors. Most stars occur in pairs, triplets or in even more complicated systems, and the Sun is among a minority of stars in being alone except for its planetary companions. It does seem, however, that a single star with a planetary system offers the greatest potential for the development of life. When there are two or more stars in the same system, any planets are likely to have unstable orbits and to suffer from wide extremes of temperature.

The Solar System's structure is thought to be typical of a star that formed in isolation. As the hot young Sun threw material outward, inner planets (Mercury, Venus, Earth and Mars) were left as small rocky bodies, whereas outer planets (Jupiter, Saturn, Uranus and Neptune) kept their lighter gases and became huge "gas giants." Jupiter has two and a half times the mass of all the other planets put together. Pluto, a small object with a strange orbit, which sometimes carries it within the orbit of Neptune, is usually regarded as a ninth planet, but some astronomers consider it to be an escaped moon of Neptune or a large asteroid.

Planetary relations

Several planets are accompanied by smaller bodies called moons or satellites. Jupiter and Saturn have at least 17 and 22 respectively, whereas Earth has its solitary Moon. Sizes vary enormously, from Ganymede, one of Jupiter's large, so-called Galilean satellites, which has a diameter of 5,000 km (3,100 miles), to Mars' tiny Deimos, which is only 8 km (5 miles) across.

The Earth's Moon is at an average distance of 384,000 km (239,000 miles) and has a diameter of 3,476 km (2,160 miles). Its mass is $\frac{1}{81}$ of the Earth's. Although it is referred to as the Earth's satellite, the Moon is large for a secondary body. Some astronomers have suggested that the Earth/Moon system is a double planet. Certain theories of the origins of the Moon propose that it was formed from the solar nebula in the same way as the Earth was and very close to it. The Moon takes 27.3 days to orbit the Earth—exactly the same time that it takes to rotate once on its axis. As a result, it presents the same face to the Earth all the time.

Our planet's orbit around the Sun is not a perfect circle but an ellipse and so its distance from the Sun varies slightly. More importantly, the Earth is tilted, so that at different times of the year one pole or another "leans" toward the Sun. Without this tilt there would be no seasons. The angle of tilt is not constant: over tens of thousands of years the axis of the Earth "wobbles" like a slowly spinning top, so that the pattern of the seasons varies over the ages. These changes have been linked to recent ice ages, which seem to occur when the northern hemisphere has relatively cool summers.

Patterns of time

The Earth's movements on its axis and around the Sun give us our basic measurements of time—the day and the year—as well as setting the rhythm of the seasons and the ice ages. One rotation of the Earth on its axis—the time from one sunrise to the next—originally defined the day, and the time taken for one complete orbit around the Sun defined the year. Today, however, scientists define both the day and the year in terms of time units "counted" by precision instruments called atomic clocks.

A third basic rhythm is set not by the Sun but by the Moon, which runs through a cycle of phases 29½ days long. This is the basis of the calendar month. But just as the modern calendar cannot cope with months 29½ days long, so too it would have trouble with the precise year, which is, inconveniently, just less than 365¼ days long. This is the reason for leap years, by means of which an extra day is added to the month of February every fourth year.

Even this system does not keep the calendar exactly in step with the Sun. Accordingly, the leap year is left out in the years which complete centuries, such as 1900, but retained when they divide exactly by 400. The year 2000 will, therefore, be a leap year. With all these corrections, the average length of the calendar year is within 26 seconds of the year defined by the Earth's movements around the Sun. Thus the calendar will be one day out of step with the heavens in the year 4906.

Cosmic rubble

The other planets are too small and too far away to produce noticeable effects on the Earth, but the smallest members of the Sun's family, the asteroids, can affect us directly. Some of them have orbits that cross the orbit of the Earth around the Sun. From time to time they penetrate the Earth's atmosphere: small fragments burn up high in the atmosphere as meteors, whereas larger pieces may survive to strike the ground as meteorites. These in fact provide an echo of times gone by. All the planets, as the battered face of the Moon shows, suffered collisions from many smaller bodies in the course of their evolution from the collapsing pre-solar gas cloud.

Eclipses occur because the Moon, smaller than the Sun, is closer to Earth and looks just as big. This means that when all three are lined up the Moon can blot out the Sun, causing a solar eclipse. When the Earth passes through the main shadow cone, or umbra, the eclipse is total; in the area of partial shadow, or penumbra, a partial eclipse is seen. A similar effect is produced when Earth passes between the Moon and the Sun, causing a lunar eclipse. At most full moons, eclipses do not occur; the Moon passes either above or below the Earth's shadow, because the Moon's orbit is inclined at an angle of 5° to the orbit of the Earth.

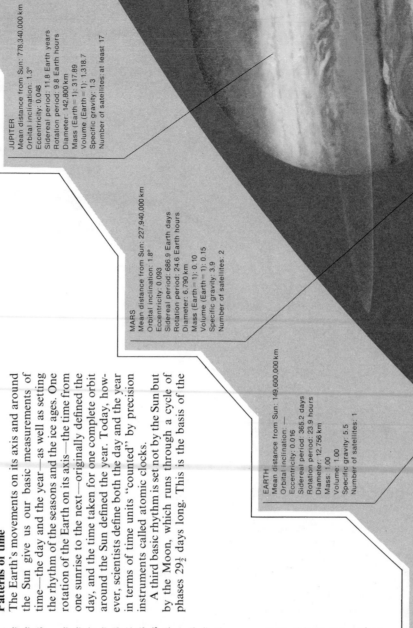

MEMBERS OF THE SOLAR SYSTEM

The Sun has nine planetary attendants. They are best compared in terms of orbital data (distance from the Sun, inclination of orbit to the Earth's orbit, and eccentricity, which means the departure of a planet's orbit from circularity); planetary periods (the time for a planet to go around the Sun—sidereal periods, and the time it takes for one axial revolution—the rotation period); and physical data (equatorial diameter, mass, volume and density or specific gravity—the weight of a substance compared with the weight of an equal volume of water).

Scale

Diameter of Sun: 1,400,000 km

MERCURY
Mean distance from Sun: 57,910,000 km
Orbital inclination: 7°
Eccentricity: 0.205
Sidereal period: 87.9 Earth days
Rotation period: 58.7 Earth days
Diameter: 4,870 km
Mass (Earth = 1): 0.05
Volume (Earth = 1): 0.05
Specific gravity: 5.5
Number of satellites: 0

VENUS
Mean distance from Sun: 108,210,000 km
Orbital inclination: 3.3°
Eccentricity: 0.006
Sidereal period: 224.7 Earth days
Rotation period: 243 Earth days
Diameter: 12,100 km
Mass (Earth = 1): 0.81
Volume (Earth = 1): 0.85
Specific gravity: 5.2
Number of satellites: 0

EARTH
Mean distance from Sun: 149,600,000 km
Orbital inclination: —
Eccentricity: 0.016
Sidereal period: 365.2 Earth days
Rotation period: 23.9 hours
Diameter: 12,756 km
Mass: 1.00
Volume: 1.00
Specific gravity: 5.5
Number of satellites: 1

MARS
Mean distance from Sun: 227,940,000 km
Orbital inclination: 1.8°
Eccentricity: 0.093
Sidereal period: 686.9 Earth days
Rotation period: 24.6 Earth hours
Diameter: 6,790 km
Mass (Earth = 1): 0.10
Volume (Earth = 1): 0.15
Specific gravity: 3.9
Number of satellites: 2

JUPITER
Mean distance from Sun: 778,340,000 km
Orbital inclination: 1.3°
Eccentricity: 0.048
Sidereal period: 11.8 Earth years
Rotation period: 9.8 Earth hours
Diameter: 142,800 km
Mass (Earth = 1): 317.89
Volume (Earth = 1): 1,318.7
Specific gravity: 1.3
Number of satellites: at least 17

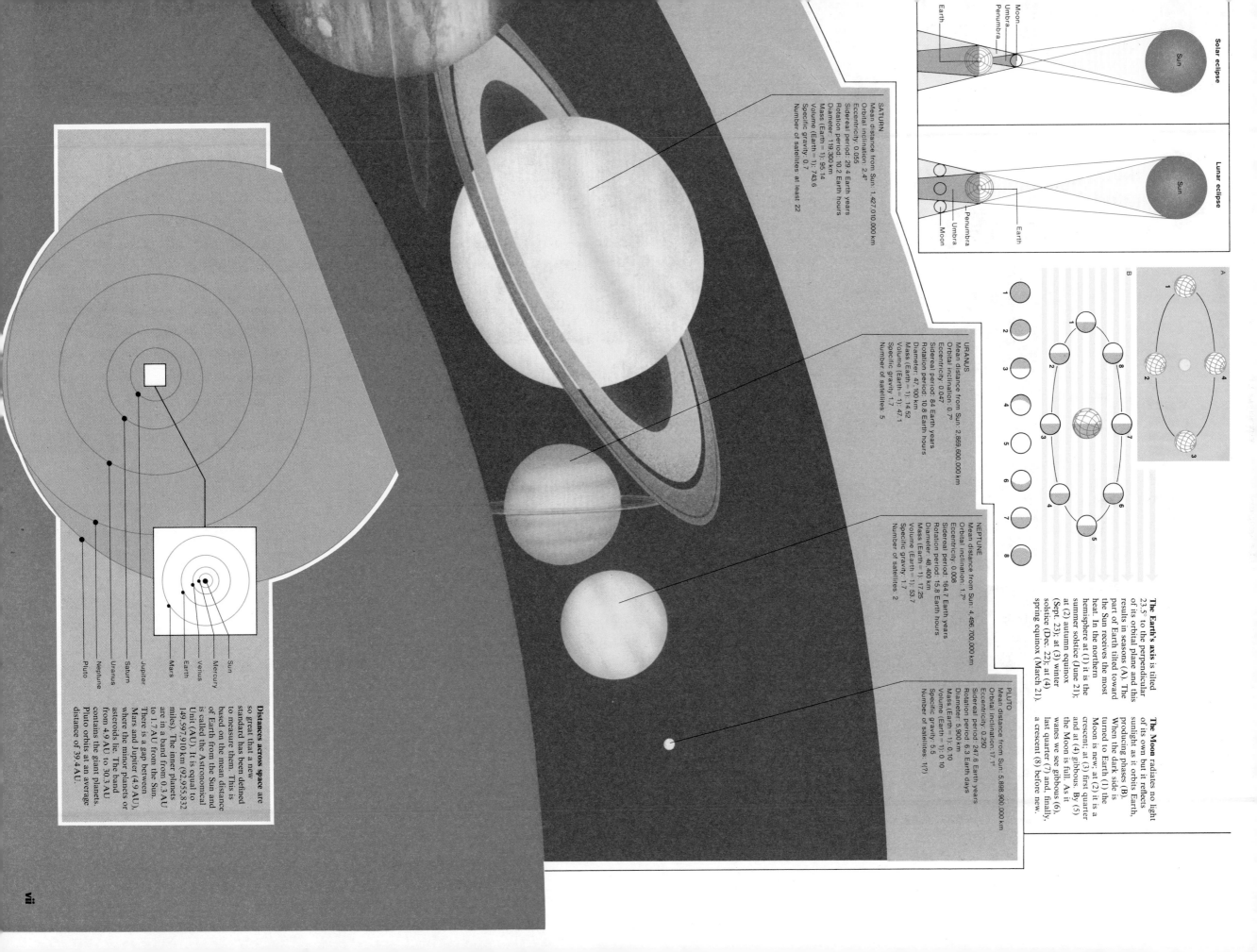

Moon
Umbra
Penumbra
Earth

Sun

Penumbra
Umbra
Earth
Moon

Sun

SATURN
Mean distance from Sun: 1,427,010,000 km
Orbital inclination: 2.4°
Eccentricity: 0.055
Sidereal period: 29.4 Earth years
Rotation period: 10.2 Earth hours
Diameter: 119,300 km
Mass (Earth = 1): 95.14
Volume (Earth = 1): 743.6
Specific gravity: 0.7
Number of satellites at least 22

URANUS
Mean distance from Sun: 2,869,600,000 km
Orbital inclination: 0.7°
Eccentricity: 0.047
Sidereal period: 84 Earth years
Rotation period: 10.8 Earth hours
Diameter: 47,100 km
Mass (Earth = 1): 14.52
Volume (Earth = 1): 47.1
Specific gravity: 1.7
Number of satellites: 5

NEPTUNE
Mean distance from Sun: 4,496,700,000 km
Orbital inclination: 1.7°
Eccentricity: 0.008
Sidereal period: 164.7 Earth years
Rotation period: 15.8 Earth hours
Diameter: 48,400 km
Mass (Earth = 1): 17.25
Volume (Earth = 1): 53.7
Specific gravity: 1.7
Number of satellites: 2

PLUTO
Mean distance from Sun: 5,898,900,000 km
Orbital inclination: 17.1°
Eccentricity: 0.250
Sidereal period: 247.6 Earth years
Rotation period: 6.3 Earth days
Diameter: 5,900 km
Mass (Earth = 1): 0.10
Volume (Earth = 1): 0.10
Specific gravity: 5.5
Number of satellites: 1(?)

Distances across space are so great that a new standard has been defined to measure them. This is based on the mean distance of Earth from the Sun and is called the Astronomical Unit (AU). It is equal to 149,597,910 km (92,955,832 miles). The inner planets are in a band from 0.3 AU to 1.7 AU from the Sun. There is a gap between Mars and Jupiter (4.9 AU), where the minor planets or asteroids lie. The band from 4.9 AU to 30.3 AU contains the giant planets. Pluto orbits at an average distance of 39.4 AU.

Sun
Mercury
Venus
Earth
Mars
Jupiter
Saturn
Uranus
Neptune
Pluto

A
B

The Earth's axis is tilted 23.5° to the perpendicular of its own orbital plane and this results in seasons (A). The part of Earth tilted toward the Sun receives the most heat. In the northern hemisphere at (1) it is the summer solstice (June 21); at (2) autumn equinox (Sept. 23); at (3) winter solstice (Dec. 22); at (4) spring equinox (March 21).

The Moon radiates no light of its own but it reflects sunlight as it orbits Earth. When the dark side is turned to Earth (1) the Moon is new; at (2) it is a crescent; at (3) first quarter and at (4) gibbous. By (5) the Moon is full. As it wanes we see gibbous (6), last quarter (7) and, finally, a crescent (8) before new.

Landsat (A) circles Earth 14 times every 24 hours at a height of 920km (570 miles). Every 25 seconds it surveys 34,250 sq km (13,225 sq mile).

Earth, Satellites and Mapping

Satellites give us a greater overview of numerous aspects of life on Earth than any earth-bound eye could see.

Of all the information gleaned from satellites, accurate weather forecasts are of particular social and economic value. The first weather satellite was Tiros 1 (Television and Infrared Observation Satellite), launched by the United States in 1960. By the time Tiros 10 ceased operations in 1967, the series had sent back more than half a million photographs, firmly establishing the value of satellite imagery.

Tiros was superseded by the ESSA (Environmental Science Services Administration) and the NOAA (National Oceanic and Atmospheric Administration) satellites. These orbited the Earth from pole to pole, and they covered the entire globe during the course of a day. Other weather satellites, such as the European Meteosat, are placed in geostationary orbit over the Equator, which means they stay in one place and continually monitor a single large region.

Watching the weather

In addition to photographing clouds, weather satellites monitor the extent of snow and ice cover, and they measure the temperature of the oceans and the composition of the atmosphere. Information about the overall heat balance of our planet gives clues to long-term climatic change, and includes the effects on climate of human activities such as the burning of fossil fuels and deforestation.

Infrared sensors allow pictures to be taken at night as well as during the day. The temperature of cloud tops, measured by infrared devices, is a guide to the height of the clouds. In a typical infrared image, high clouds appear white because they are the coldest, lower clouds and land areas appear gray, and oceans and lakes are black. Information on humidity in the atmosphere is provided by sensors tuned to wavelengths between 5.5 and 7 micrometers, at which water vapor strongly absorbs the radiation.

To "see" inside clouds, where infrared and visible light cannot penetrate, satellites use sensors tuned to short-wavelength radio waves (microwaves) around the 1.5 centimeter wavelength. These sensors can reveal whether or not clouds will give rise to heavy rainfall, snow or hail. Microwave sensors are also useful for locating ice floes in polar regions, making use of the different microwave reflections from land ice, sea ice and open water.

Satellites that send out such pictures are in relatively low orbits, at a height of about 1,000 km (620 miles), and they pass over each part of the Earth once every 12 hours. But to build up a global model of the Earth's weather and climate, meteorologists need continual information on wind speed and direction at various levels in the atmosphere, together with temperature and humidity profiles. This data is provided by geostationary satellites. Cloud photographs taken every half-hour give information on winds, and computers combine this with temperature and humidity soundings to give as complete a model as is possible of the Earth's atmosphere.

Increasing attention is also being paid to the Earth's surface, notably by means of a series of satellites called Landsat (originally ERTS or Earth Resource Technology Satellites), the first of which was launched by the United States in 1972. The third and current Landsat is in a similar pole-to-pole orbit as the weather satellites, but its cameras are more powerful and they make more detailed surveys of the Earth. Landsat rephotographs each part of the Earth's surface every 18 days.

How to map resources

The satellite has two sensor systems: a television camera, which takes pictures of the Earth using visible light; and a device called a multispectral scanner, which scans the Earth at several distinct wavelengths, including visible light and infrared. Data from the various channels of the multispectral scanner can be combined to produce so-called false-color images, in which each wavelength band is assigned a color (not necessarily its real one) to emphasize features of interest.

An important use of Landsat photographs is for making maps, particularly of large countries with remote areas that have never been adequately surveyed from the ground. Several countries, including Brazil, Canada and China, have set up ground stations to receive Landsat data directly. Features previously unknown or incorrectly mapped, including rivers, lakes and glaciers, show up readily on Landsat images. Urban mapping and hence planning are aided by satellite pictures that can distinguish areas of industry, housing and open parkland.

Landsat photographs have also proved invaluable for agricultural land-use planning. They are used for estimates of soil types and for determining land-use patterns. Areas of crop disease or dying vegetation are detectable by their different colors. Yields of certain crops such as wheat can now be accurately predicted from satellite imagery, so that at last it is becoming possible to keep track of the worldwide production of vital food crops. Fresh water, too, is one of our most valuable resources, and knowing its sources and seasonal variation is vital to irrigation projects.

Finally, the geologist and mineral prospector have benefited from remote sensing. Features such as fault lines and different types of sediments and rocks show up clearly on Landsat pictures. This allows geologists to select promising areas in which the prospector can look for mineral deposits.

Another way to study the Earth is by bouncing radar beams off it. Radar sensing indicates the nature of soil or rock on land and movement of water at sea, for example. This was not done by Landsat, but by equipment aboard the United States' Skylab and by a short-lived American satellite called Seasat. The Soviet Union has included Earth surveying in its Salyut program, and resource mapping is also a feature of the spacelab aboard the American space shuttle. All these activities help man to manage the limited resources on our planet and to preserve the environment.

MAPPING AND MEASURING

Man has been looking at Earth from satellites since the beginning of the 1960s, and has firmly established the value of surveys from space to those engaged in a variety of earthly pursuits. Chief of these activities are resource management, ranging from monitoring the spread of deserts and river silting to locating likely mineral deposits; environmental protection, which includes observing delicate ecosystems and natural disasters; and a whole range of mapping and land-use planning.

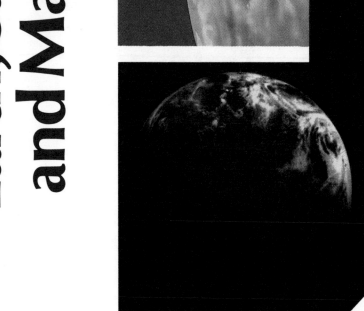

al scanner (B)
ating mirror
ses visible on
radiation on
(2). This
intensity of
into a
electronics unit
a series of
voltage
bers that can
computer.

4 22 33 24 36 | 22 13 12 9 13 69 5 33

The numbers (C) are then transmitted back to a receiving station (D) as a radio frequency at the rate of 15 million units a second. The numbers are translated back into the digital voltage pattern and converted by computer (E) into the equivalent binary numbers, each of which represents a color.

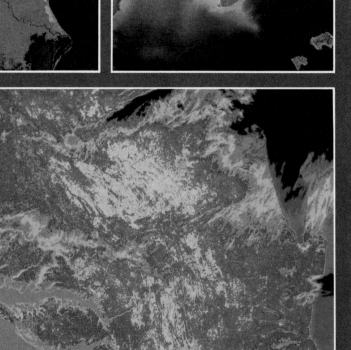

Observation of waterways and coastal areas

Observation of waterways and coastal areas (above) shows pollution and deposition of sediments. This is of importance to the fishing industry. Fish congregate in areas where upwelling brings nutrients to the surface, for example. The large yellow-orange halo around Akimiski Island in James Bay (A)—a southern extension of Hudson Bay in Canada—is fine sediment resulting from wave action on a silty shore. Seeing the sediment in this way helps to determine current patterns in the Bay. In a predominantly desert area, the Nile delta (B) stands out dramatically. The red is an intensively cultivated area: cotton is the main crop. The larger irrigation canals can be seen on the photograph. Thermal imagery, or heat capacity mapping, is used to identify rocks, to study the effects of urban 'heat islands,' to estimate soil moisture and snow melt.

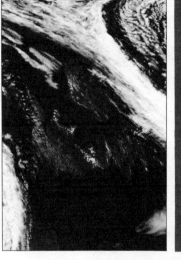

and to map shallow ground water. In this photograph of the northeast coast of North America (C) purple represents the coldest temperatures—in Lakes Erie and Ontario. The coldest parts of the Atlantic Ocean are deep blue, whereas warmer waters near the coast are light blue. Green is the warmer land, but also the Gulf Stream in the lower right part of the image. Brown, yellow and orange represent successively warmer land surface areas. Red is hot regions around cities and coal-mining regions found in eastern Pennsylvania (to the upper left of center in the picture); and, finally, gray and white are the very hottest areas—the urban heat islands of Baltimore, Philadelphia and New York City. Black areas in the upper left are cold clouds. The temperature range of the image is about 30°C (55°F).

The Earth seen from space

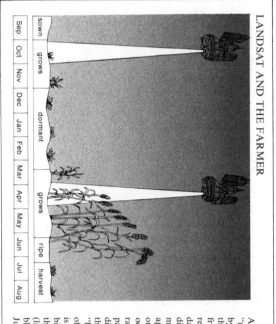

The Earth seen from space shows phases just like the Moon, Mercury and Venus do to us. These dramatic photographs were taken from a satellite moving at 35,885 km (22,300 miles) above South America at 7.30 am (1), 10.30 am (2), noon (3), 3.30 pm (4) and at 10.30 pm (5), and clearly show the Earth in phase.

LANDSAT AND THE FARMER

Agriculturists benefit from "multitemporal analysis" by satellites (left). This is the comparison of data from the same field recorded on two or more dates. It is also able to differentiate crops, which may have an identical appearance, or signature, on one day, but on another occasion exhibit different rates of growth. The pattern of growth is different for small grains than most other crops. A "biowindow" is the period of time in which vegetation is observed. These three biowindows (right) show the emergence and ripening (light blue to red to dark blue) of wheat in May, July and August.

Sep	Oct	Nov	Dec	Jan	Feb	Mar	Apr	May	Jun	Jul	Aug
sown	grows			dormant			grows			ripe	harvest

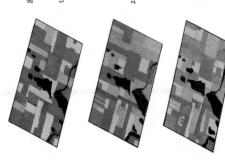

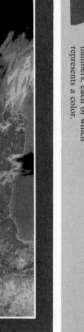

A Landsat image is made up of very many points, each of which is obtained by means of the procedure described above. Each number in the image (F) represents the radiation from a small area of land, or pixel. 0.44 hectares (1.1 acres) in size. A computer then translates the numbers into different colors, or into different shades of one color, which are projected on to a TV screen (G) and the image is seen for the first time. Finally, photographs of this false-color image are produced (H). This picture, showing a forest fire in the Upper Peninsula, Michigan, is of use to those engaged in forest management. Other satellite data of use in forestry include types of trees, patterns of growth and the spread of disease.

Weather satellite imagery

Weather satellite imagery can save lives and property by giving advance warning of bad weather conditions, as well as providing day-to-day forecasts. This Tiros image (left) shows a cold front moving west of Ireland with low-level wave clouds over southern and central England. There are low-pressure systems over northern France and to the northwest of Ireland.

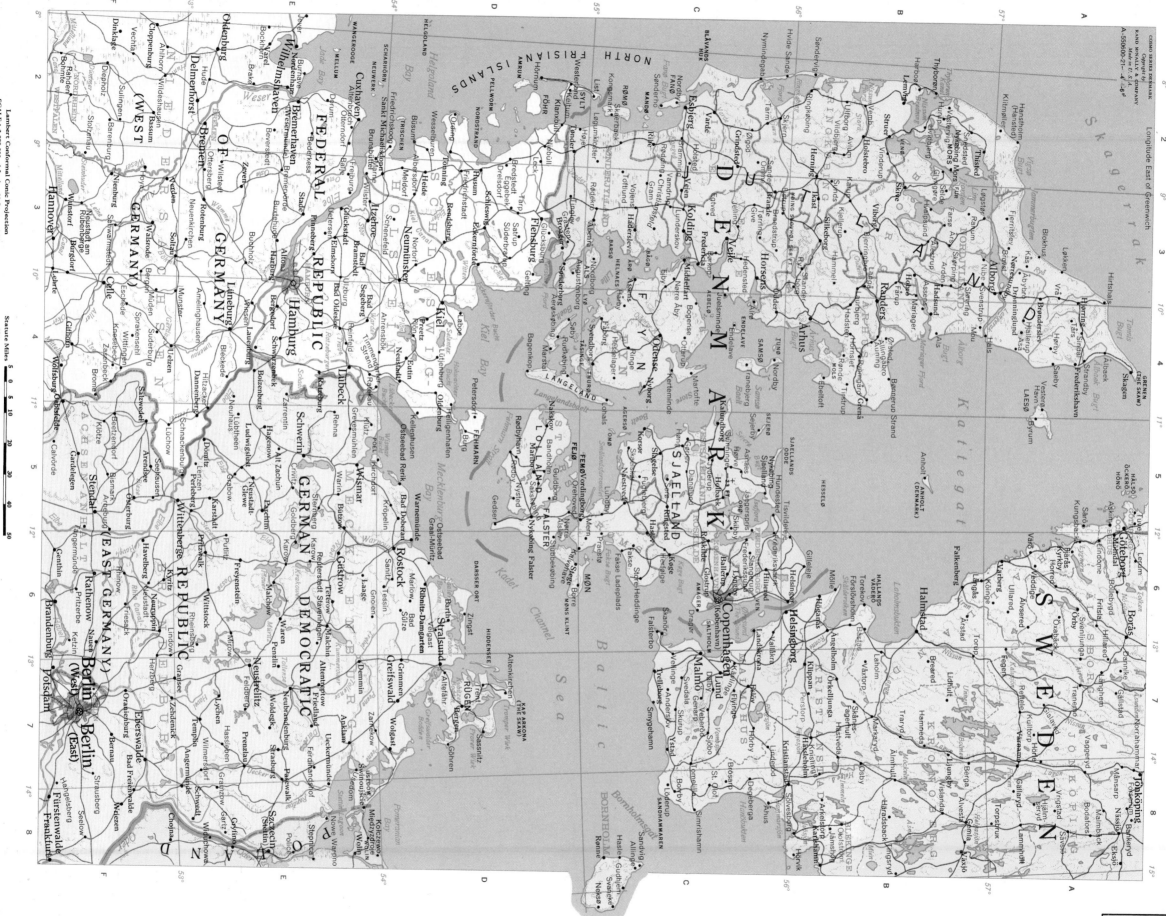

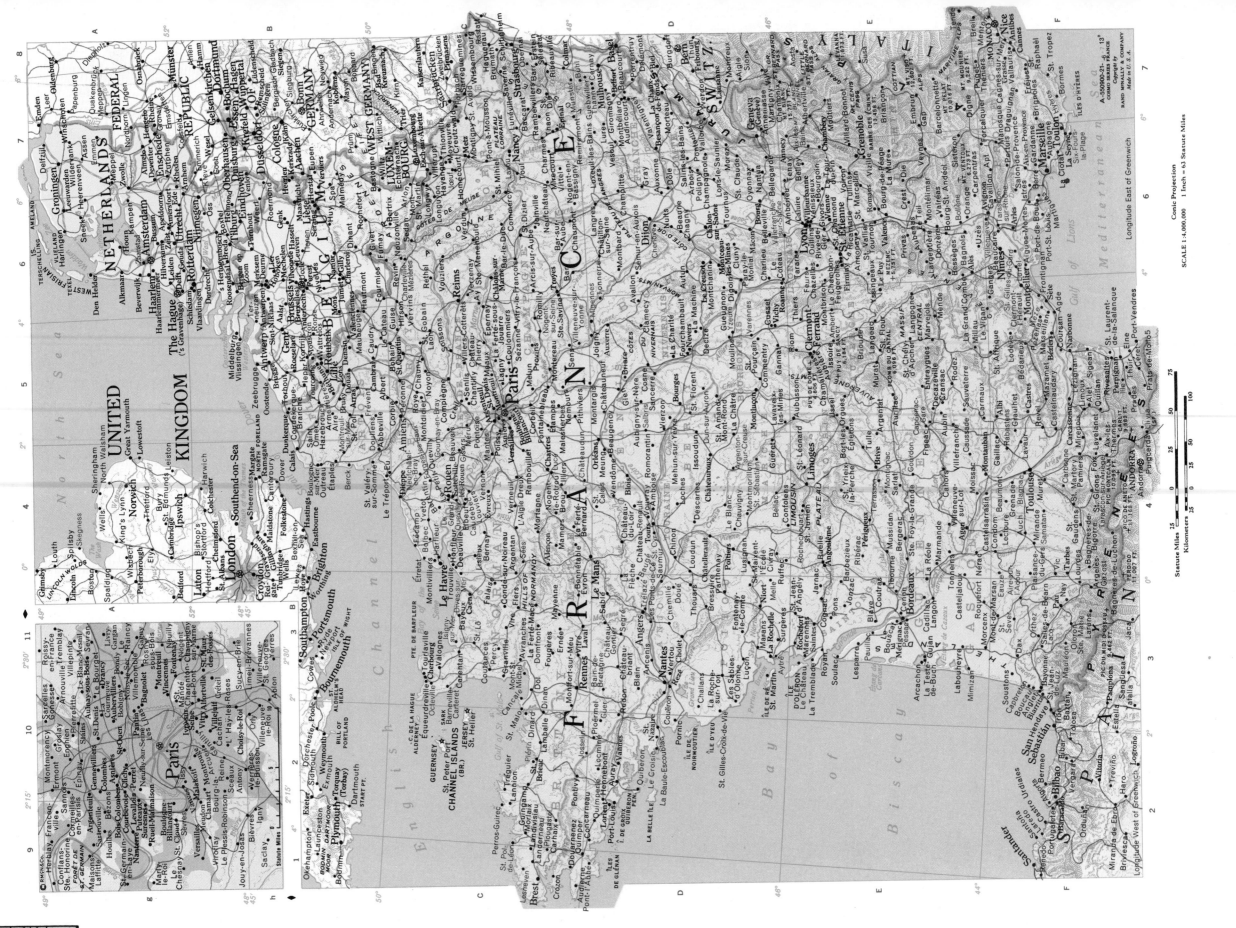

FRANCE AND THE LOW COUNTRIES

Conic Projection

SCALE 1:4,000,000   1 Inch = 63 Statute Miles

16

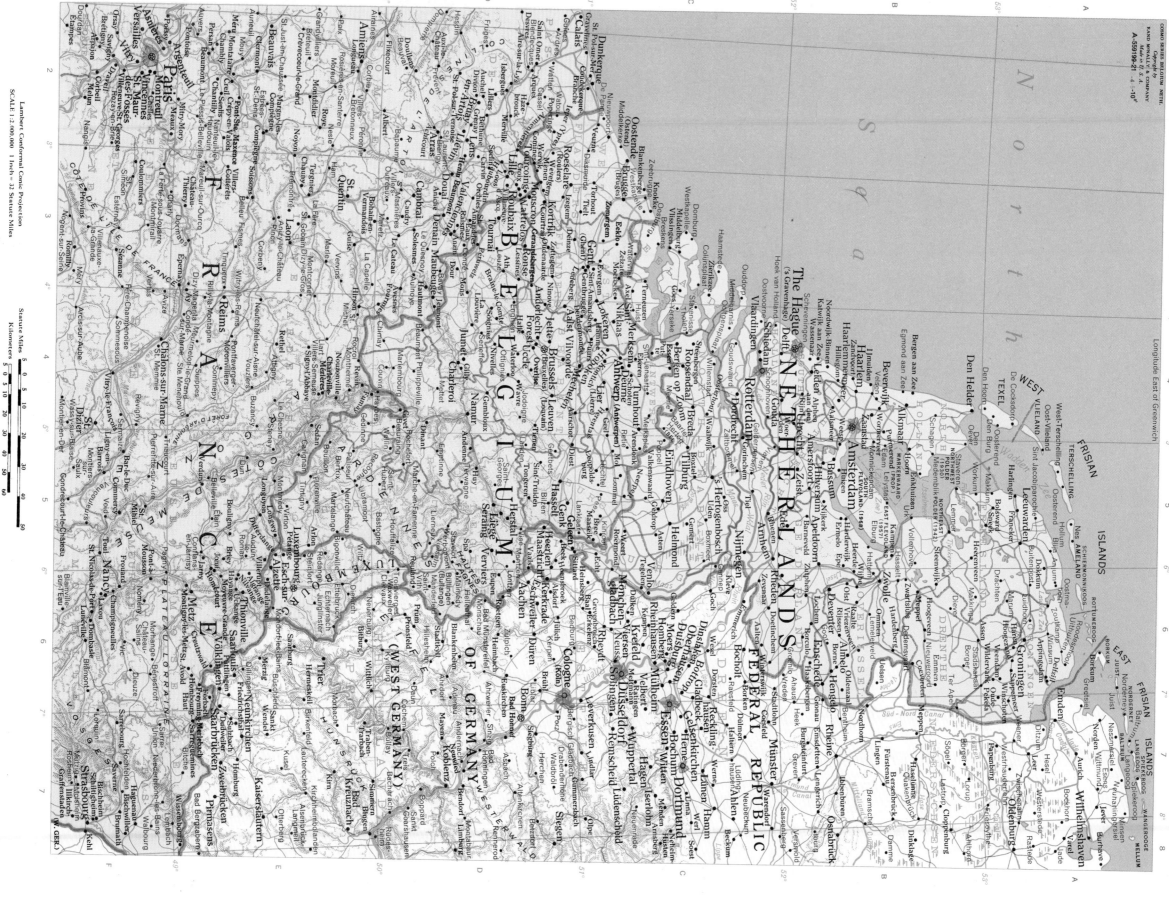

BELGIUM, NETHERLANDS, LUXEMBOURG AND WESTERN GERMANY

COSMO SERIES BELGIUM, NETH.
Copyright by
RAND McNALLY & COMPANY
Made in U. S. A.
A-559199-21 -4-10"

SCALE 1:2,000,000

Lambert Conformal Conic Projection
1 Inch = 32 Statute Miles

GERMANY, AUSTRIA AND SWITZERLAND

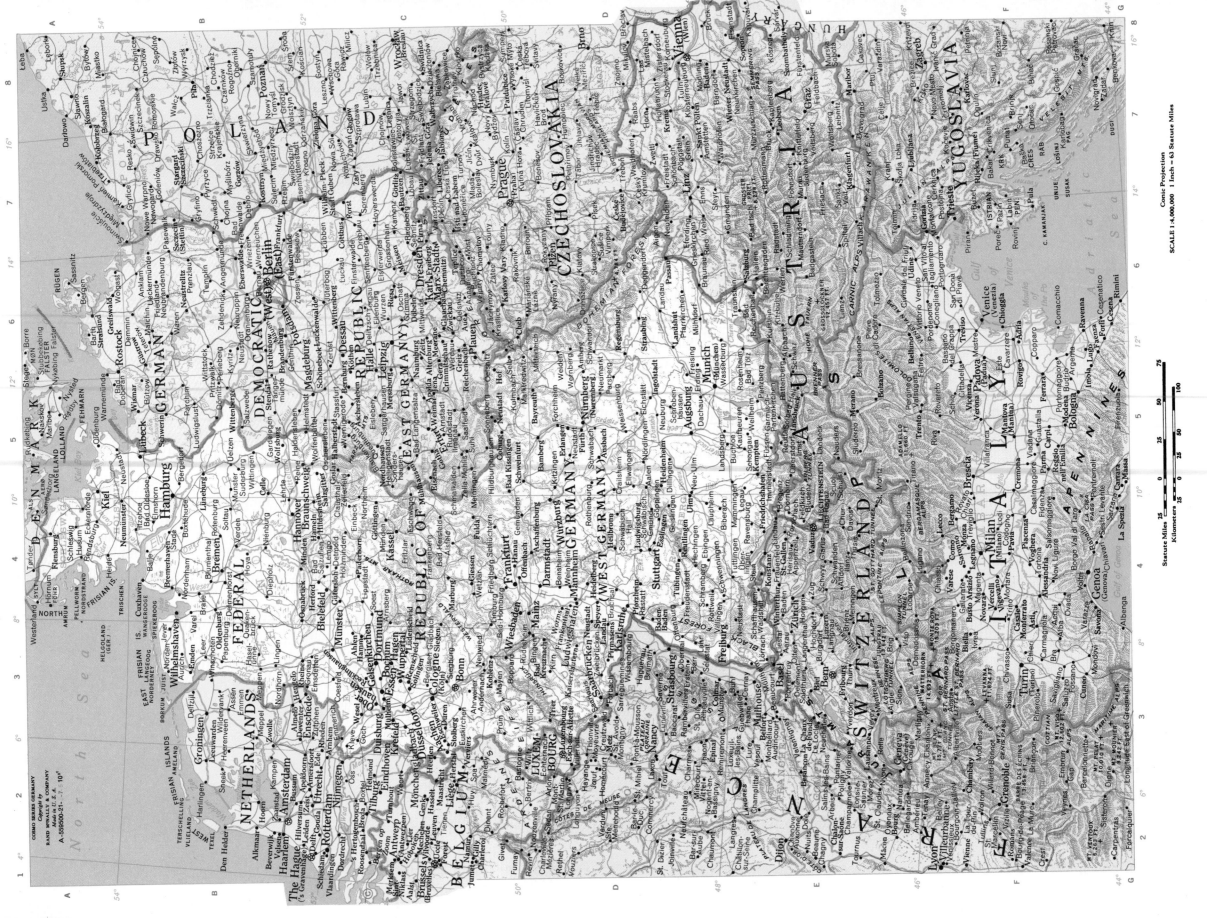

SCALE 1:4,000,000   1 Inch = 63 Statute Miles

Conic Projection

18

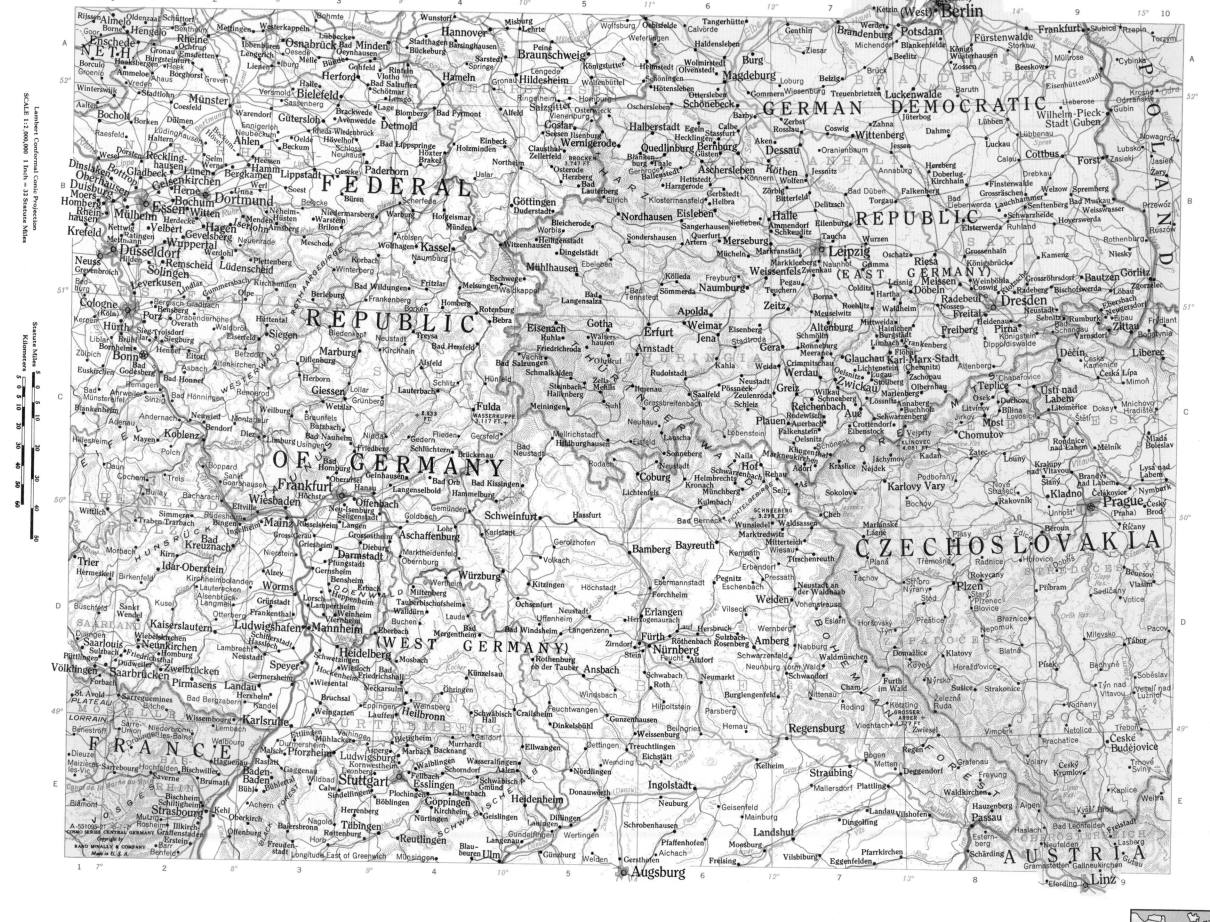

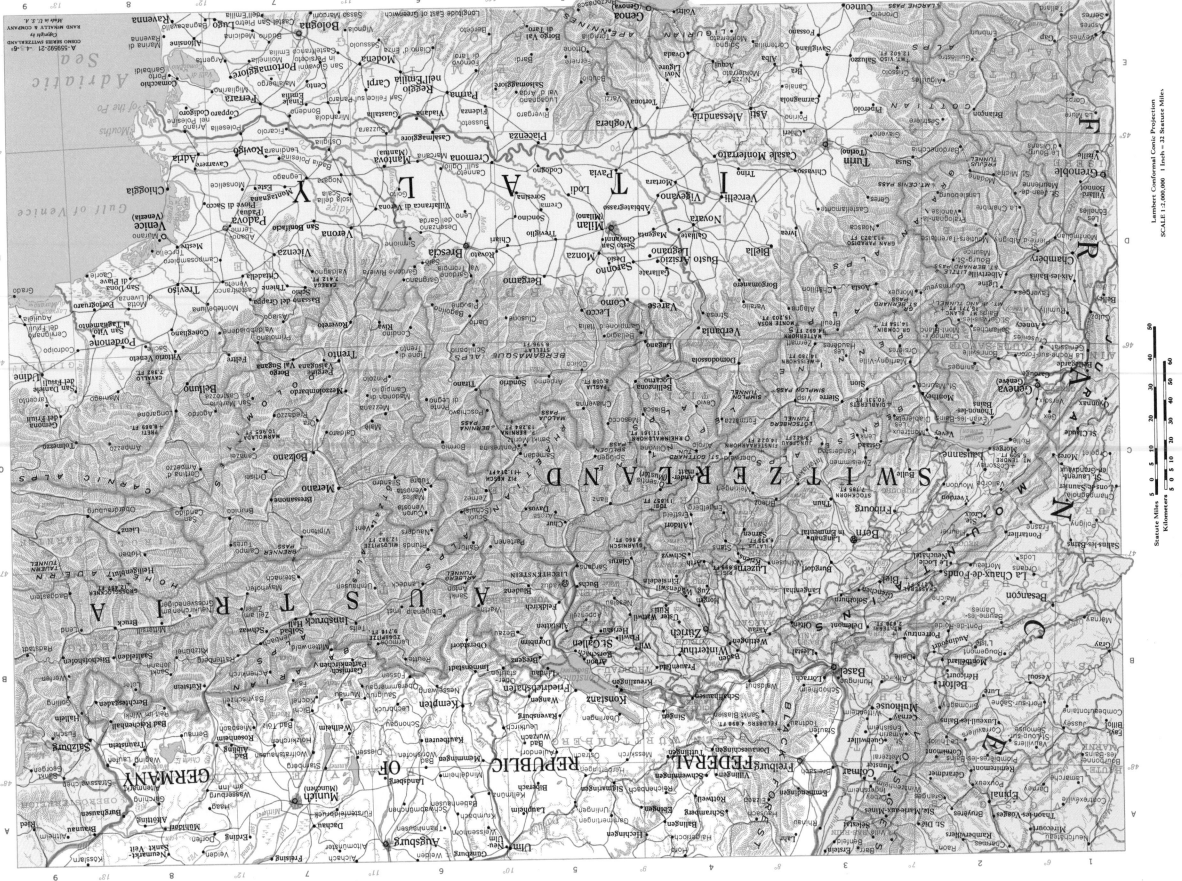

ALPINE REGIONS

Lambert Conformal Conic Projection
SCALE 1:2,000,000   1 Inch = 32 Statute Miles

20

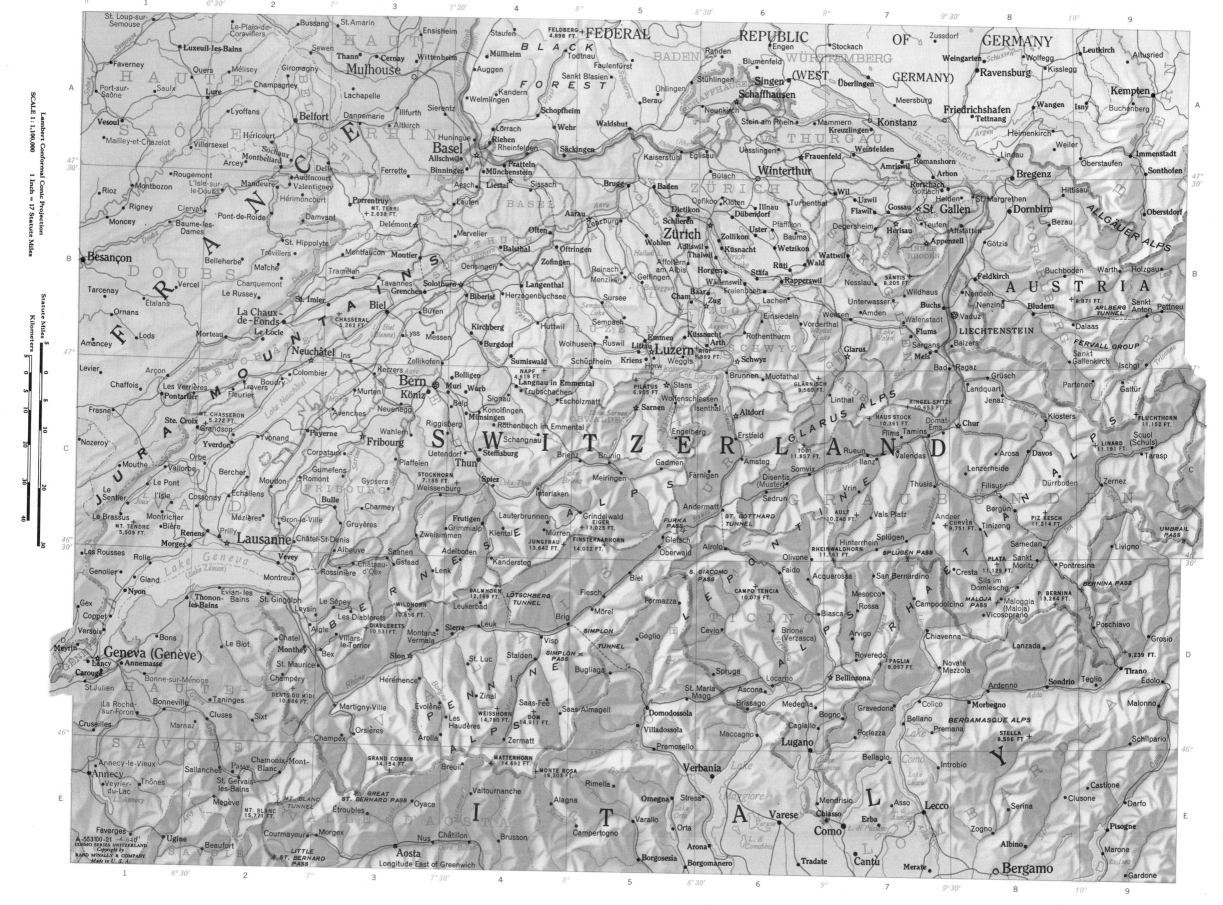

SWITZERLAND

21

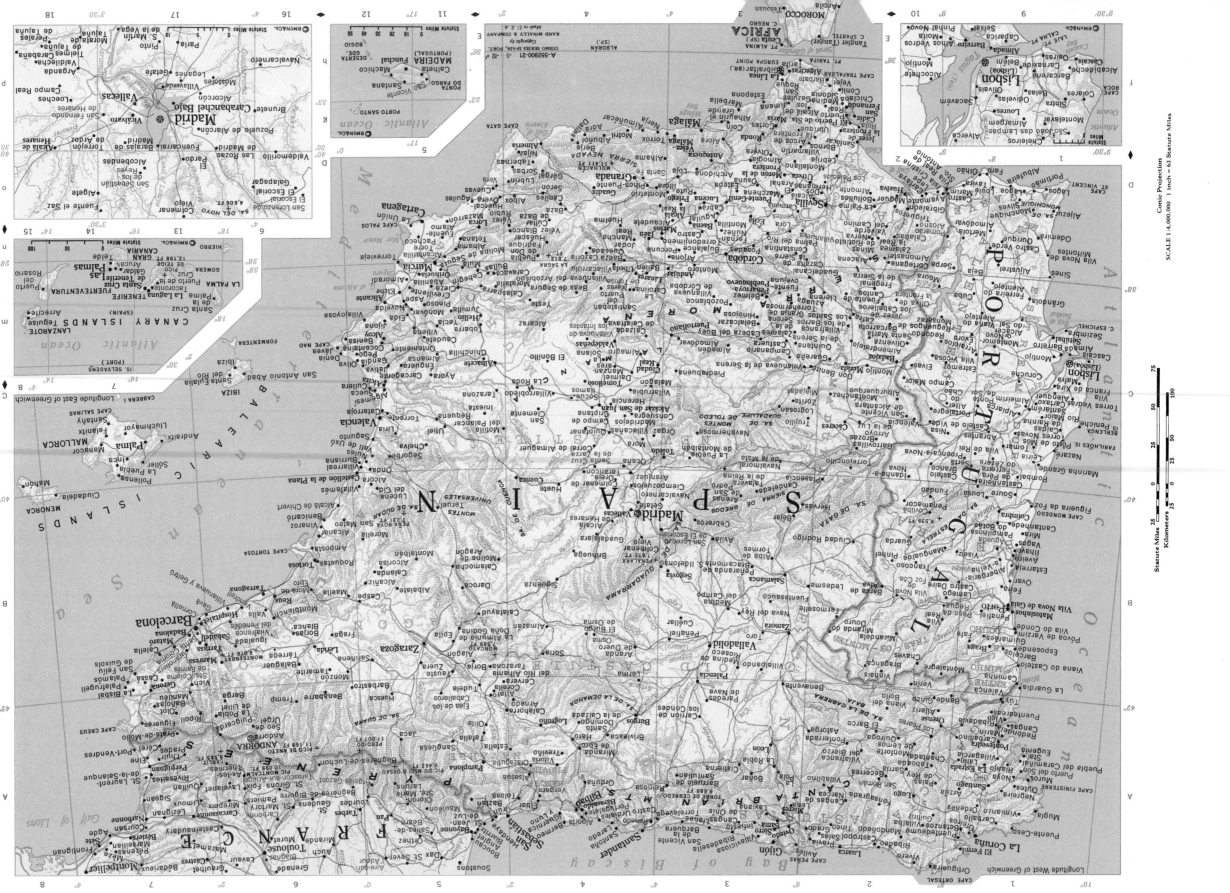

SPAIN AND PORTUGAL

SCALE 1:4,000,000   1 inch = 63 Statute Miles

Conic Projection

22

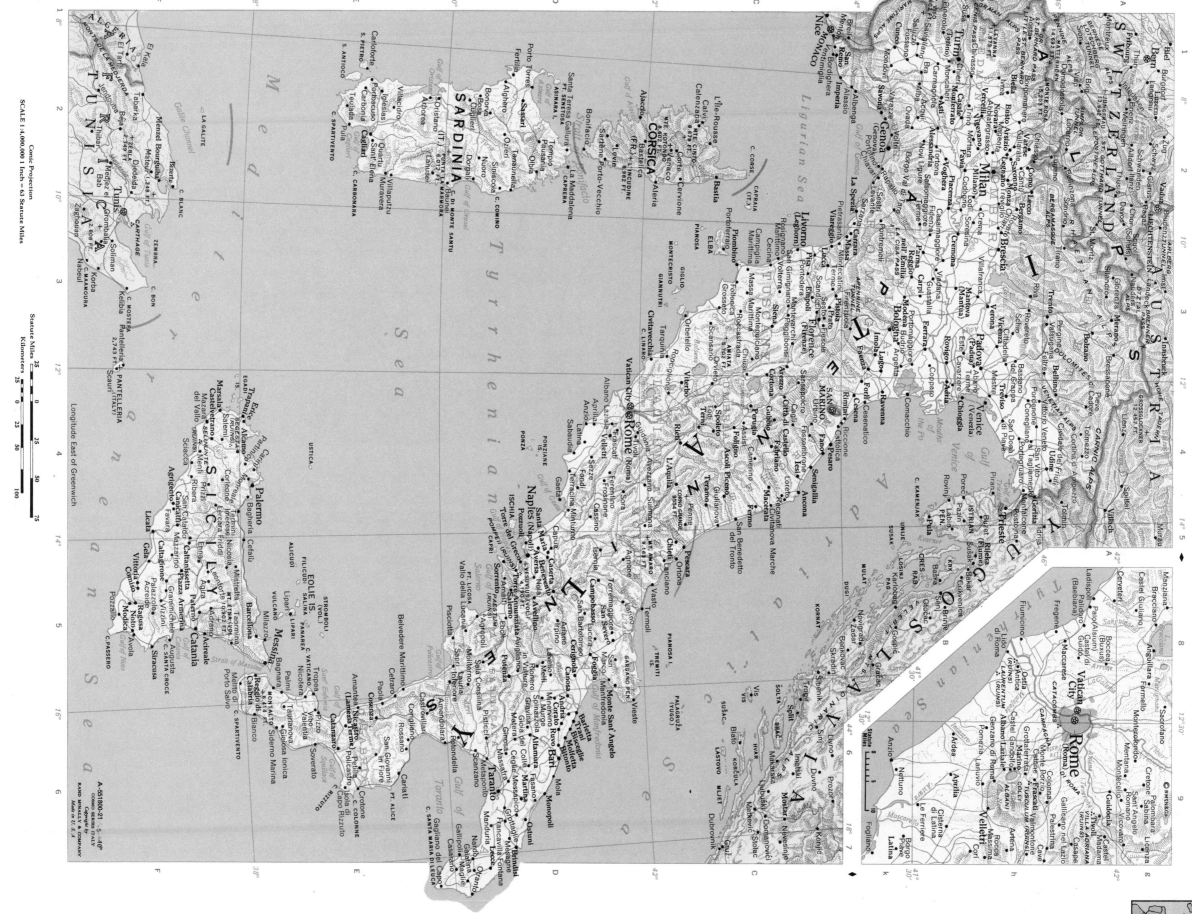

ITALY

23

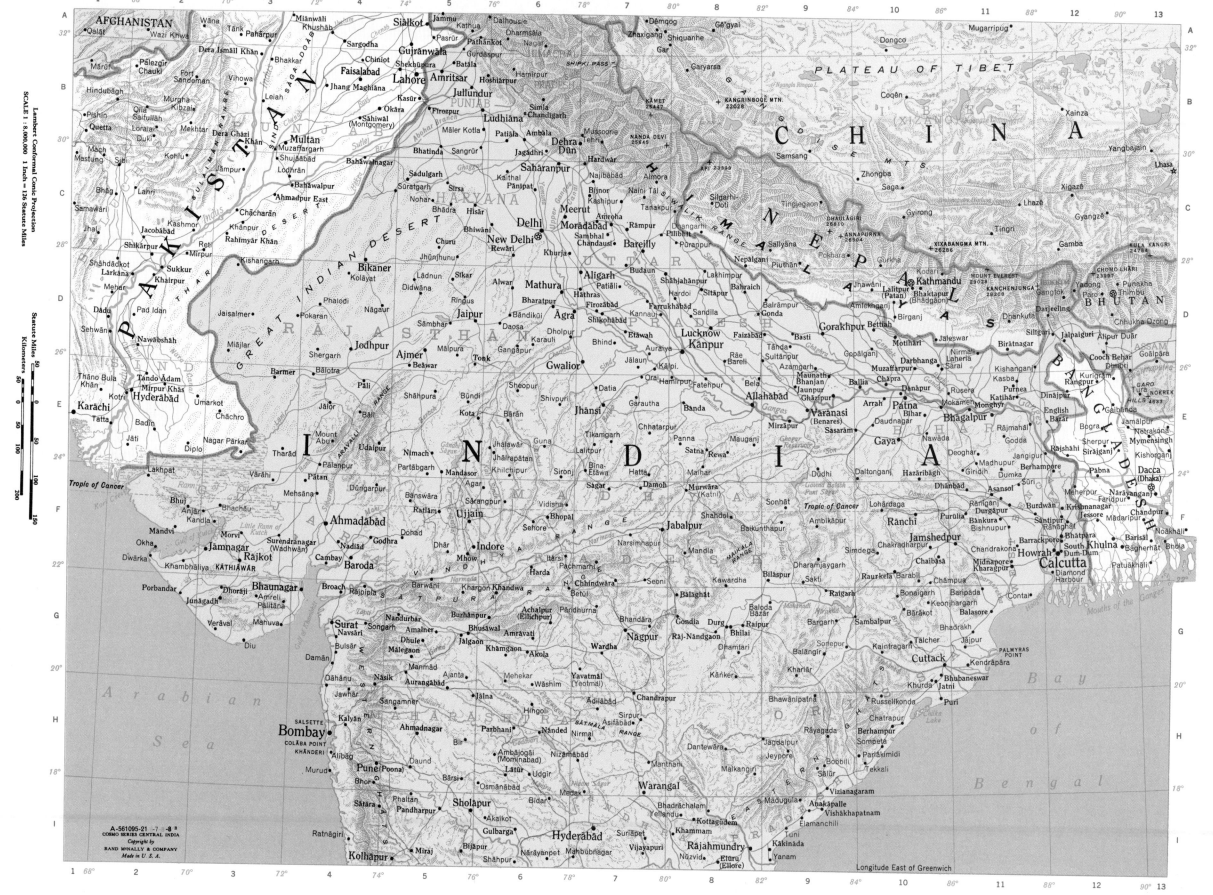

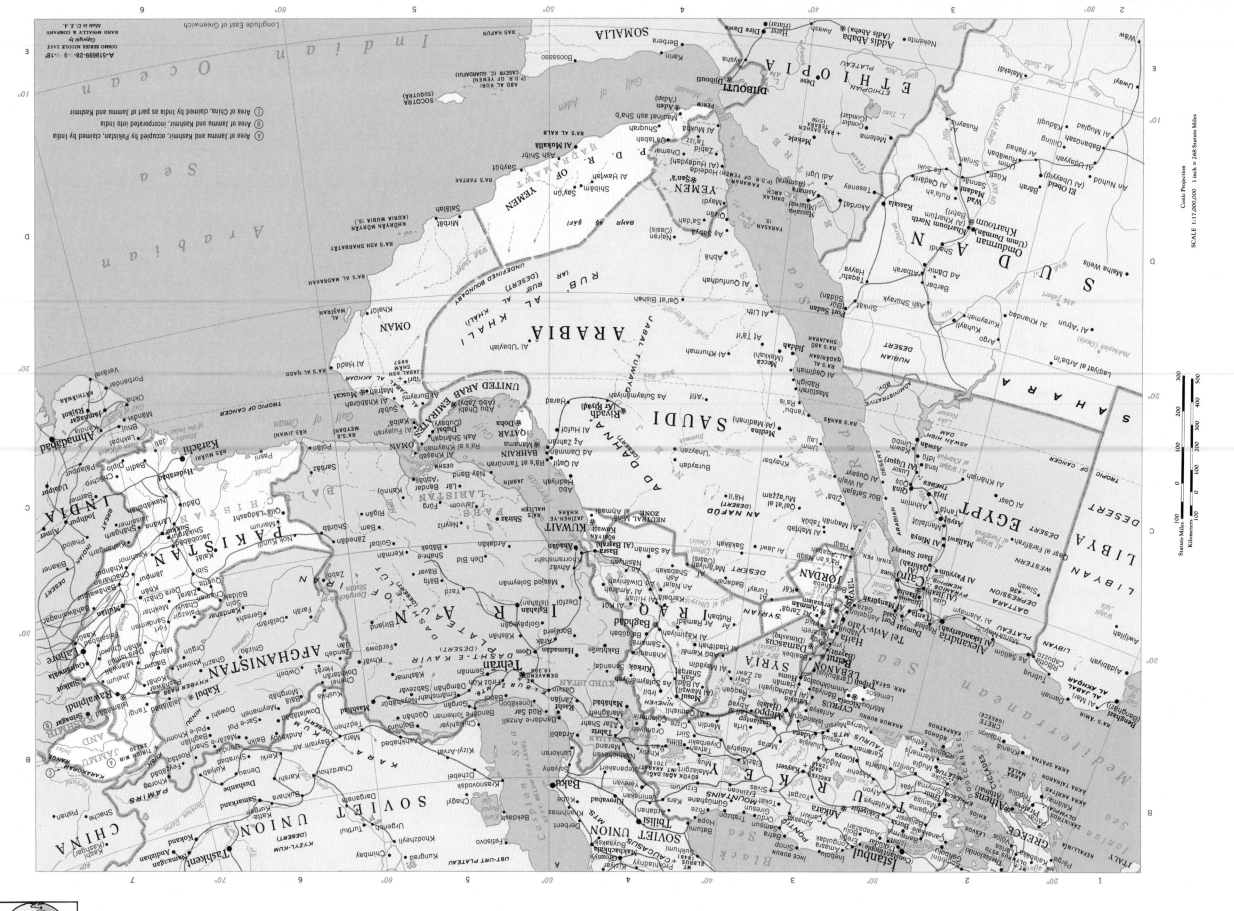

MIDDLE EAST

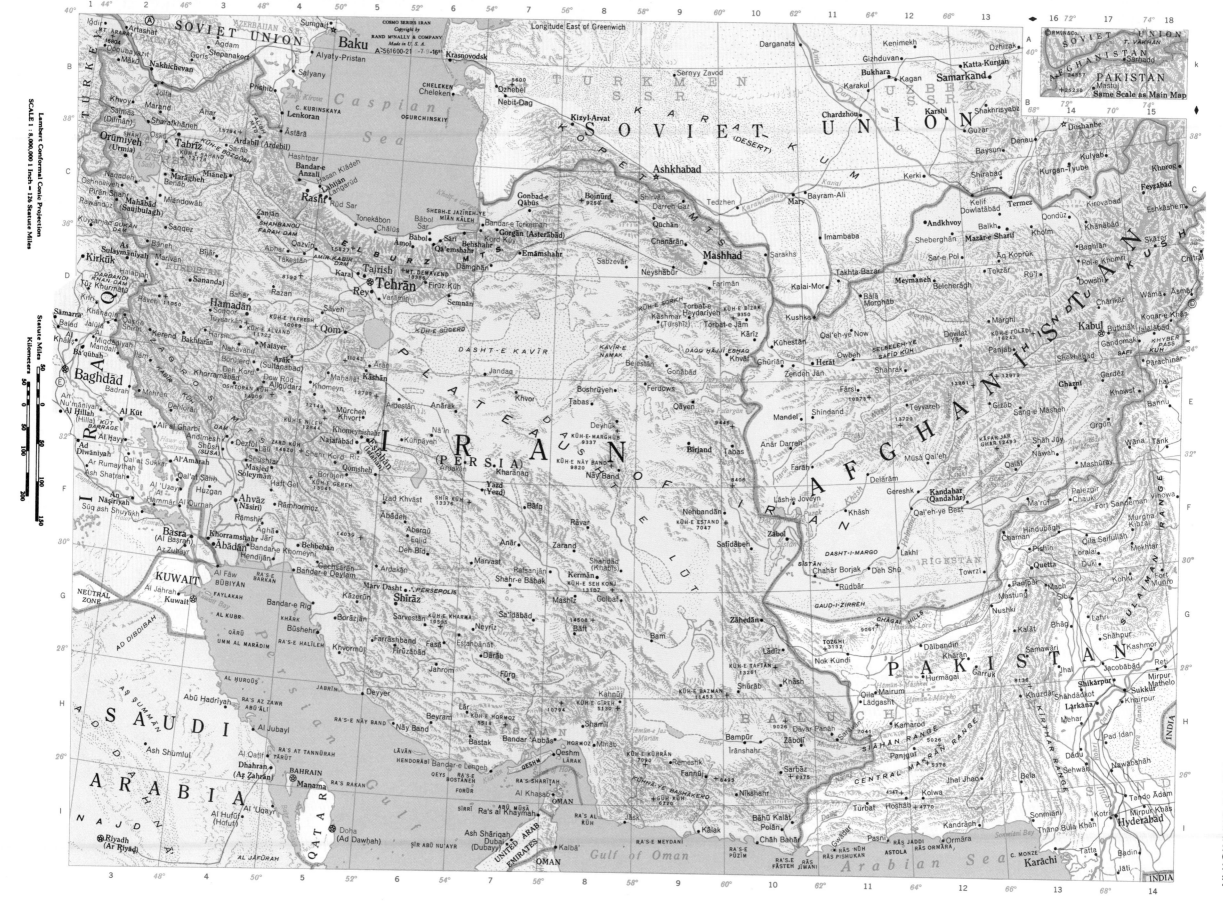

IRAN AND AFGHANISTAN

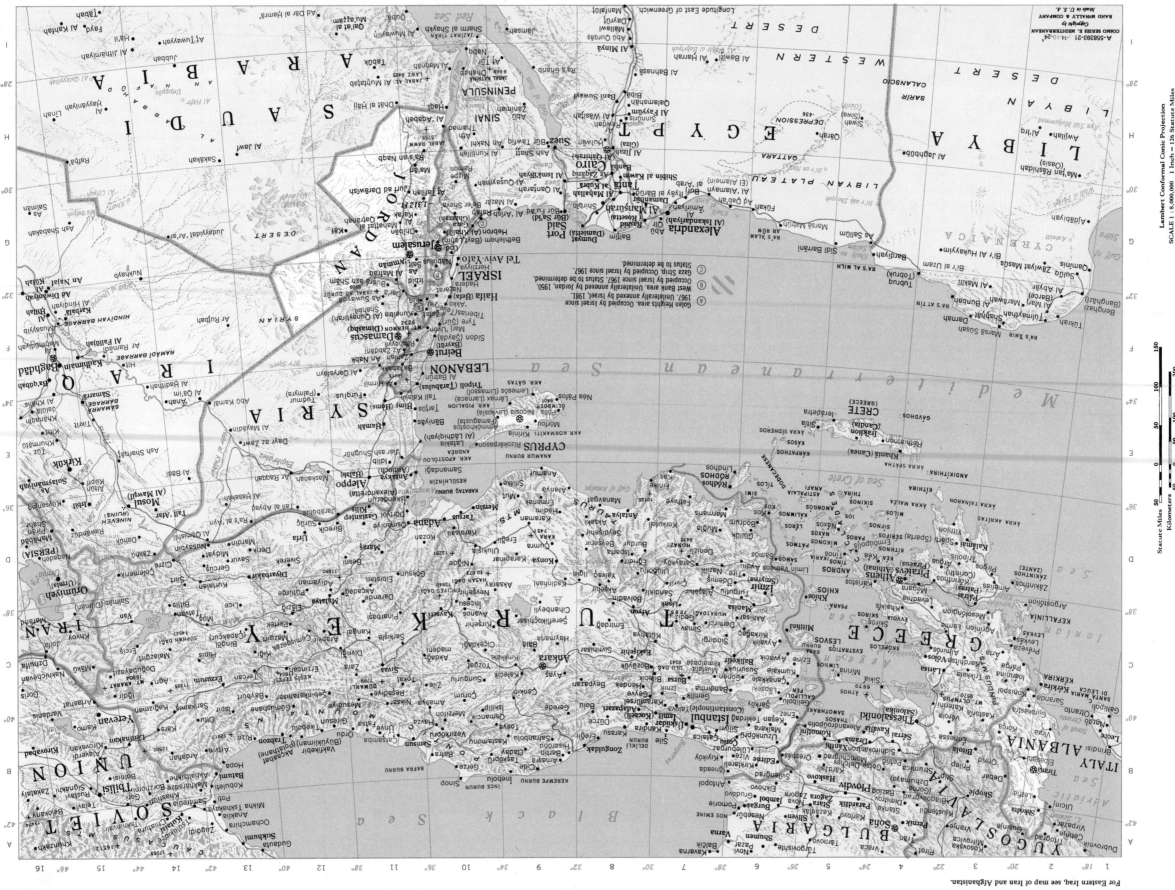

TURKEY, CYPRUS, SYRIA, JORDAN, ISRAEL AND LEBANON

For Eastern Iraq, see map of Iran and Afghanistan.

Lambert Conformal Conic Projection
SCALE 1 : 8,000,000   1 Inch = 126 Statute Miles

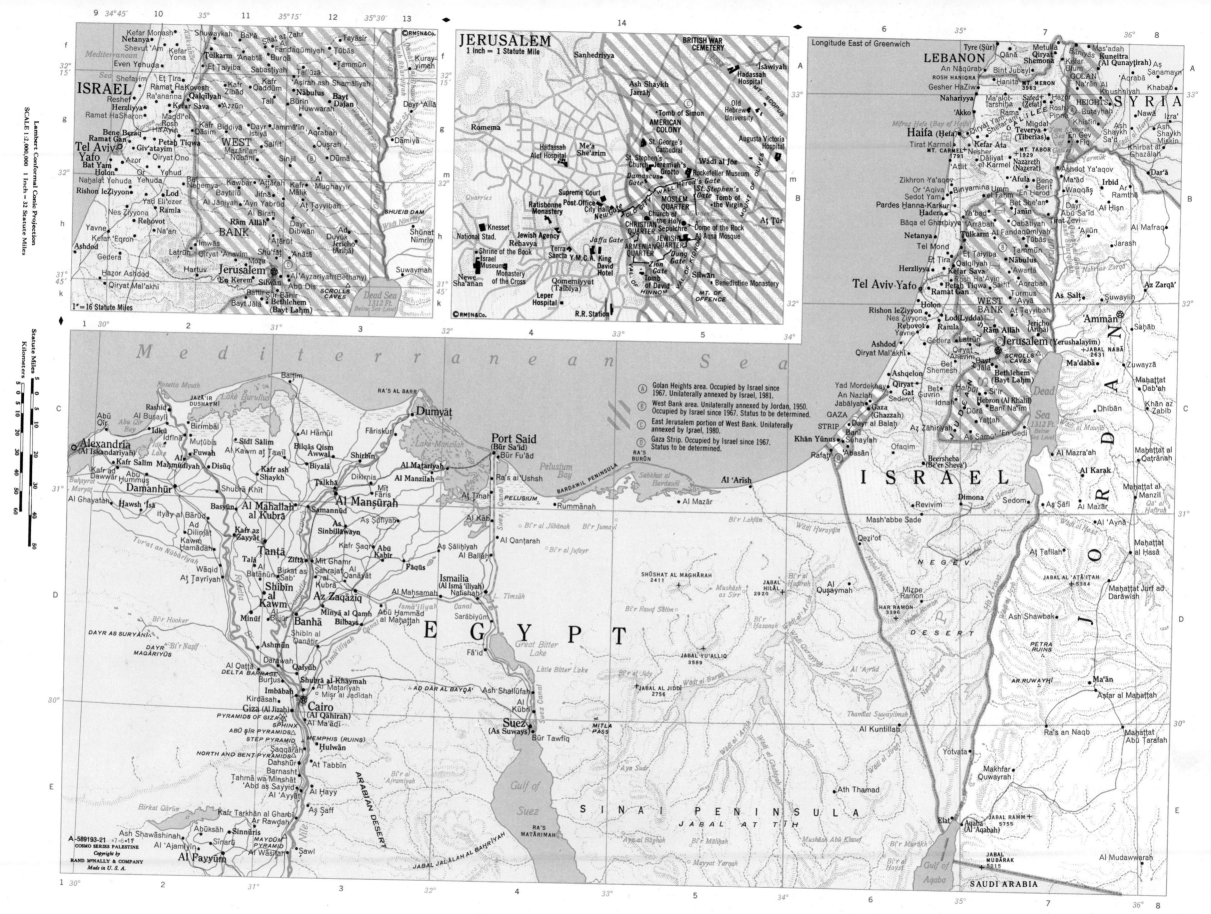

ISRAEL AND NORTHERN EGYPT

AFRICA

A-580000-21-‑11‑46⁰
COSMO SERIES AFRICA
Copyright by
RAND McNALLY COMPANY
Made in U.S.A.

Sinusoidal Projection

SCALE 1:36,313,000 1 Inch = 565 Statute Miles

Statute Miles
100 0 100   300   500   700   900
Kilometers
100 0 100 300   500   700   900 1100 1300

42

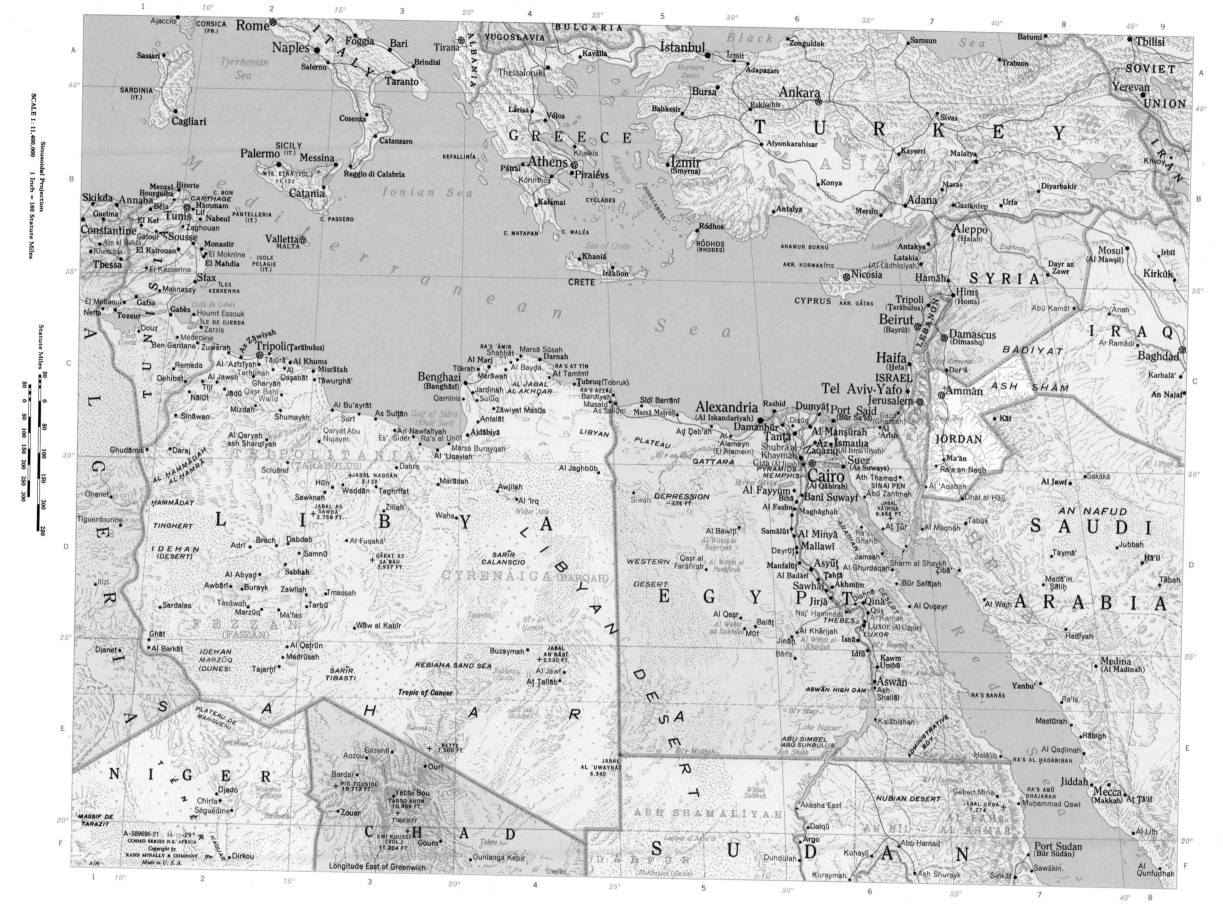

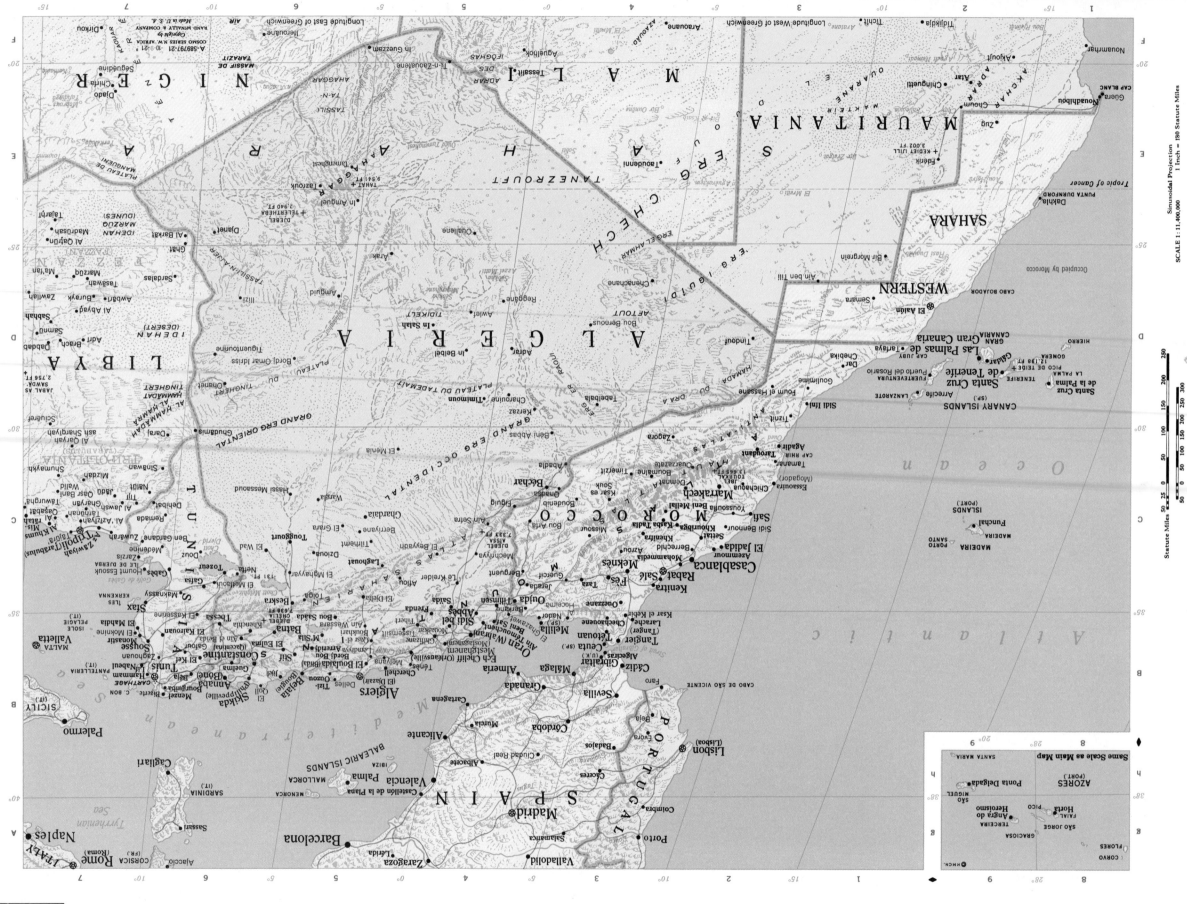

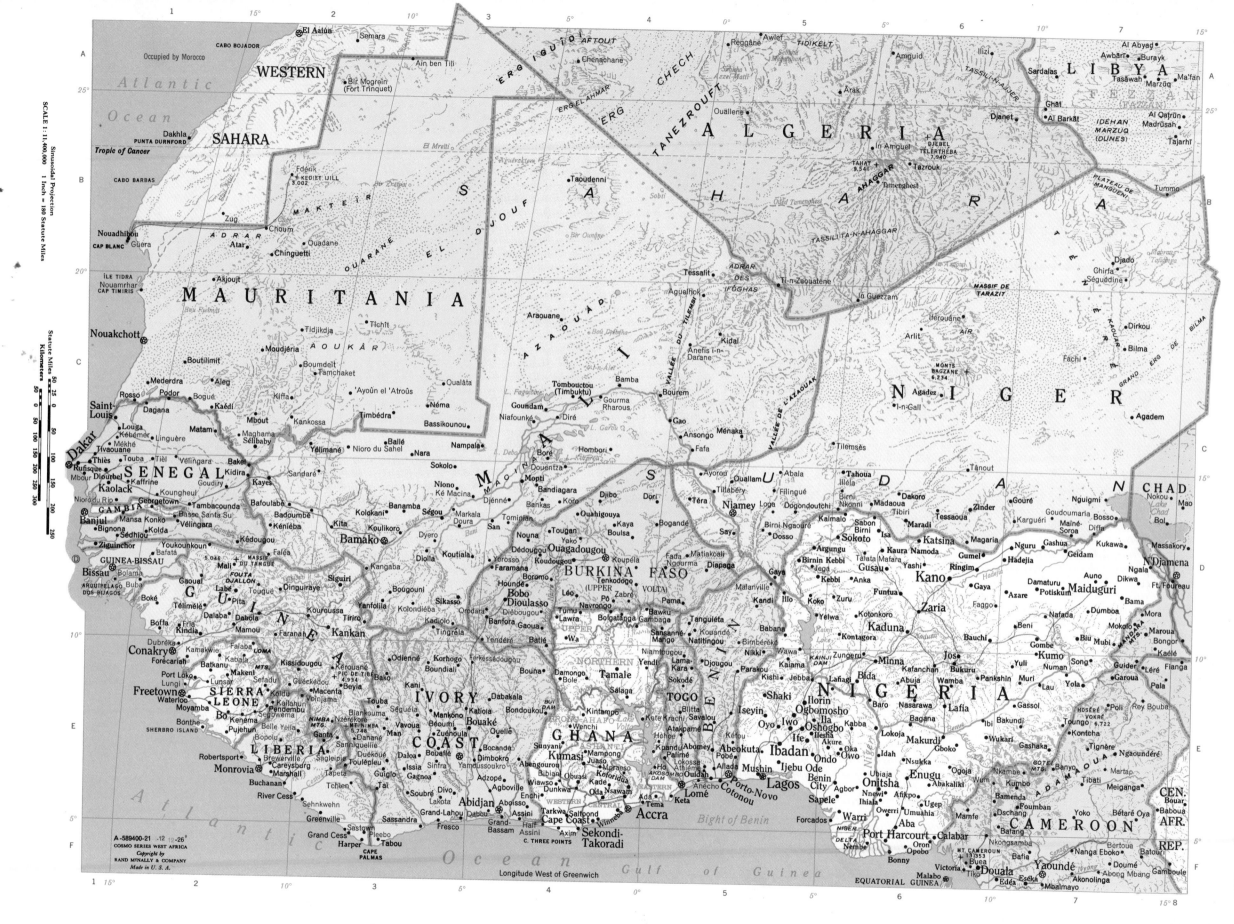

EQUATORIAL AFRICA

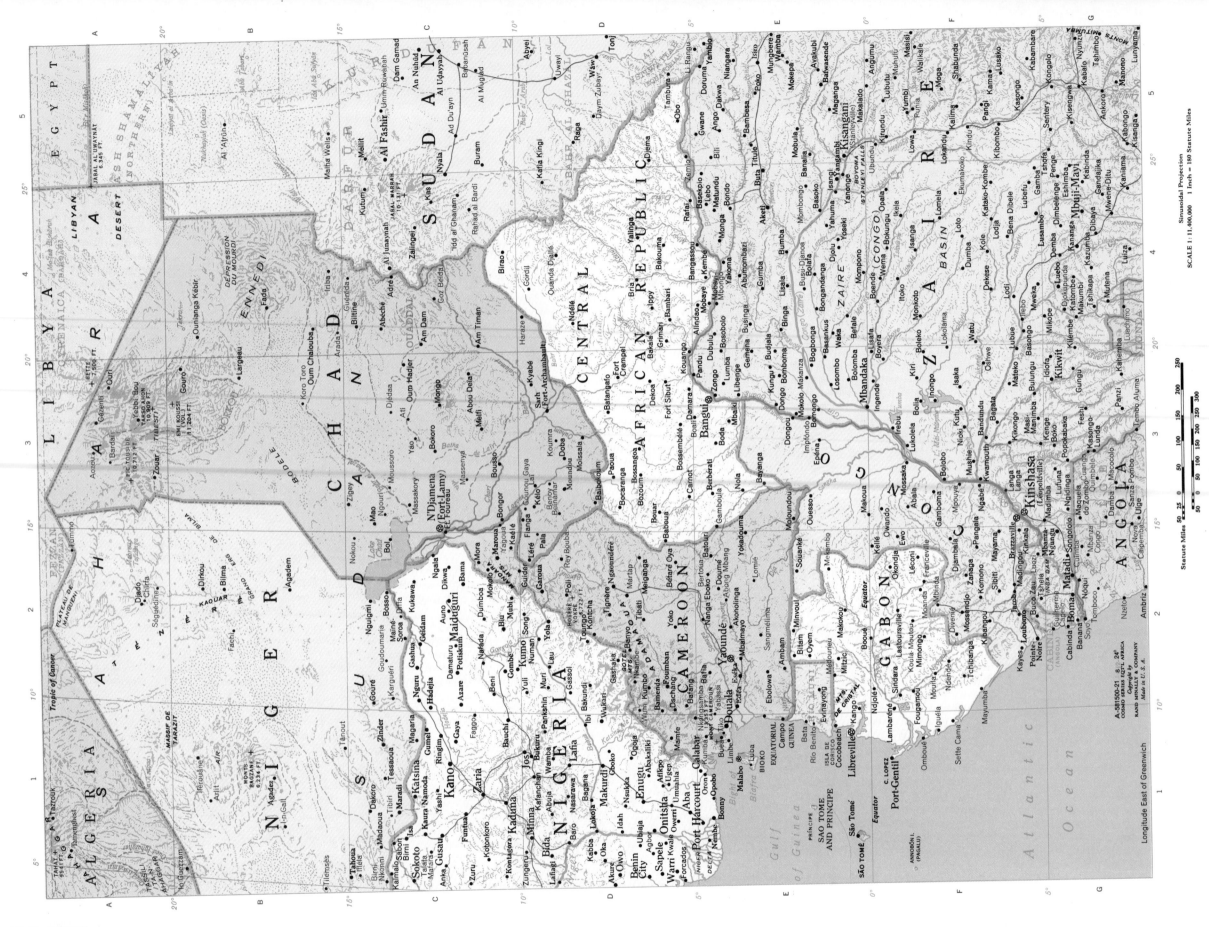

Sinusoidal Projection

SCALE 1:11,400,000   1 Inch = 180 Statute Miles

Statute Miles

Longitude East of Greenwich

46

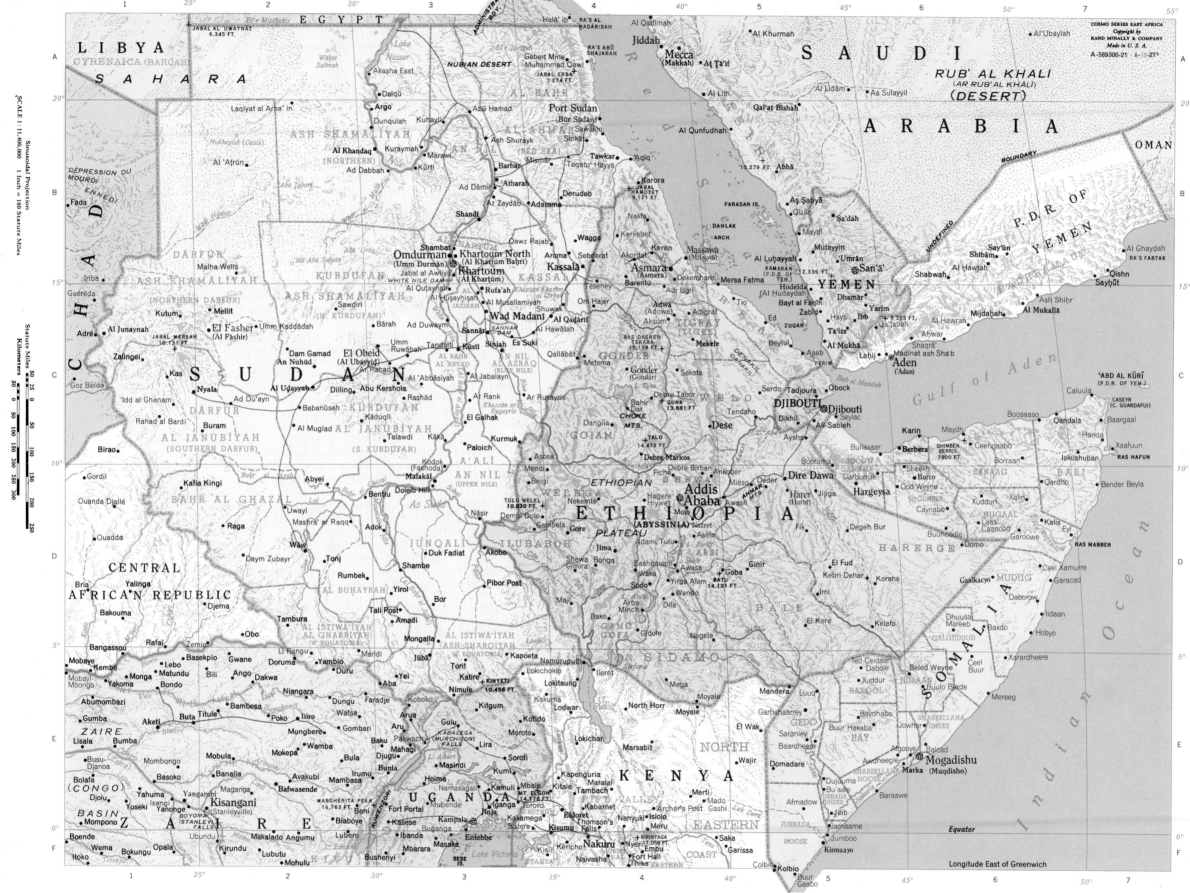

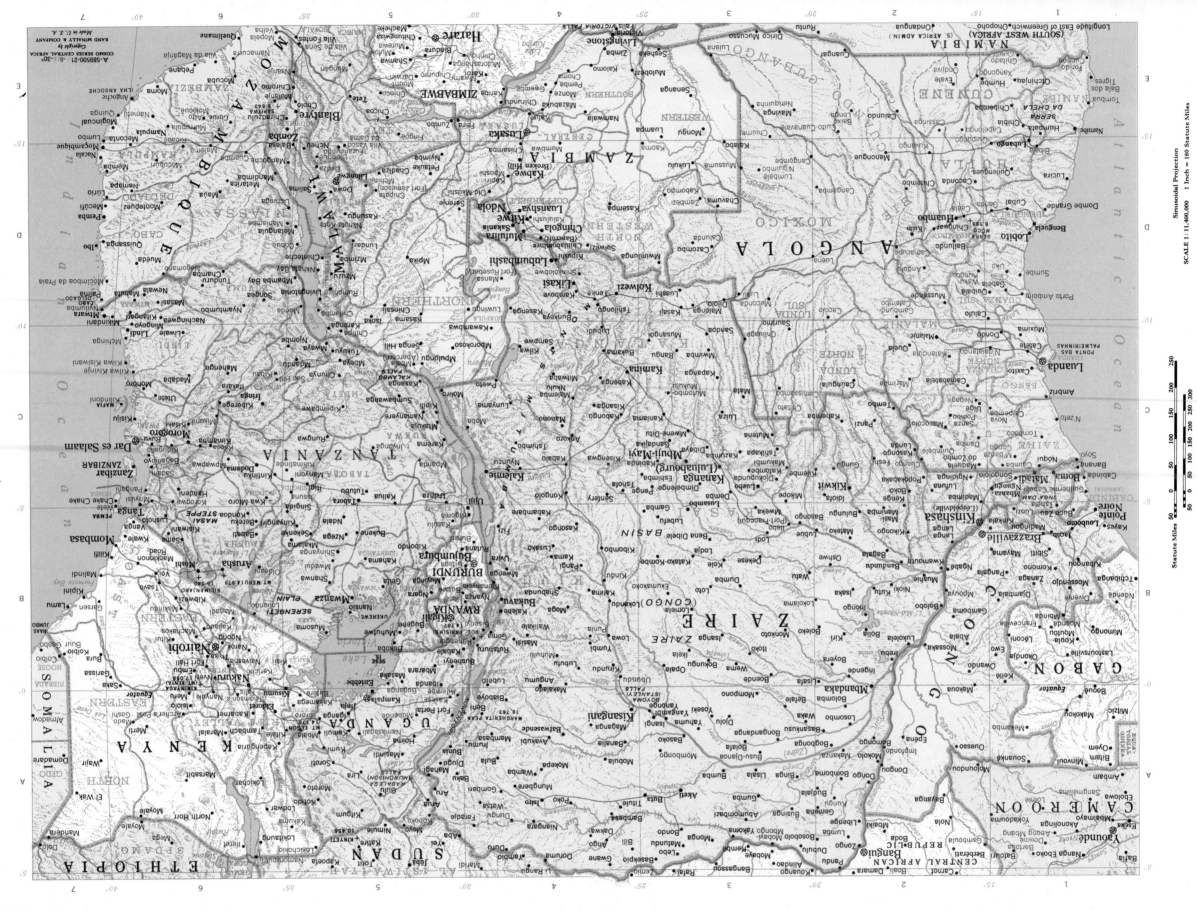

CENTRAL AFRICA

SCALE 1:11,400,000   1 Inch = 180 Statute Miles
Sinusoidal Projection

48

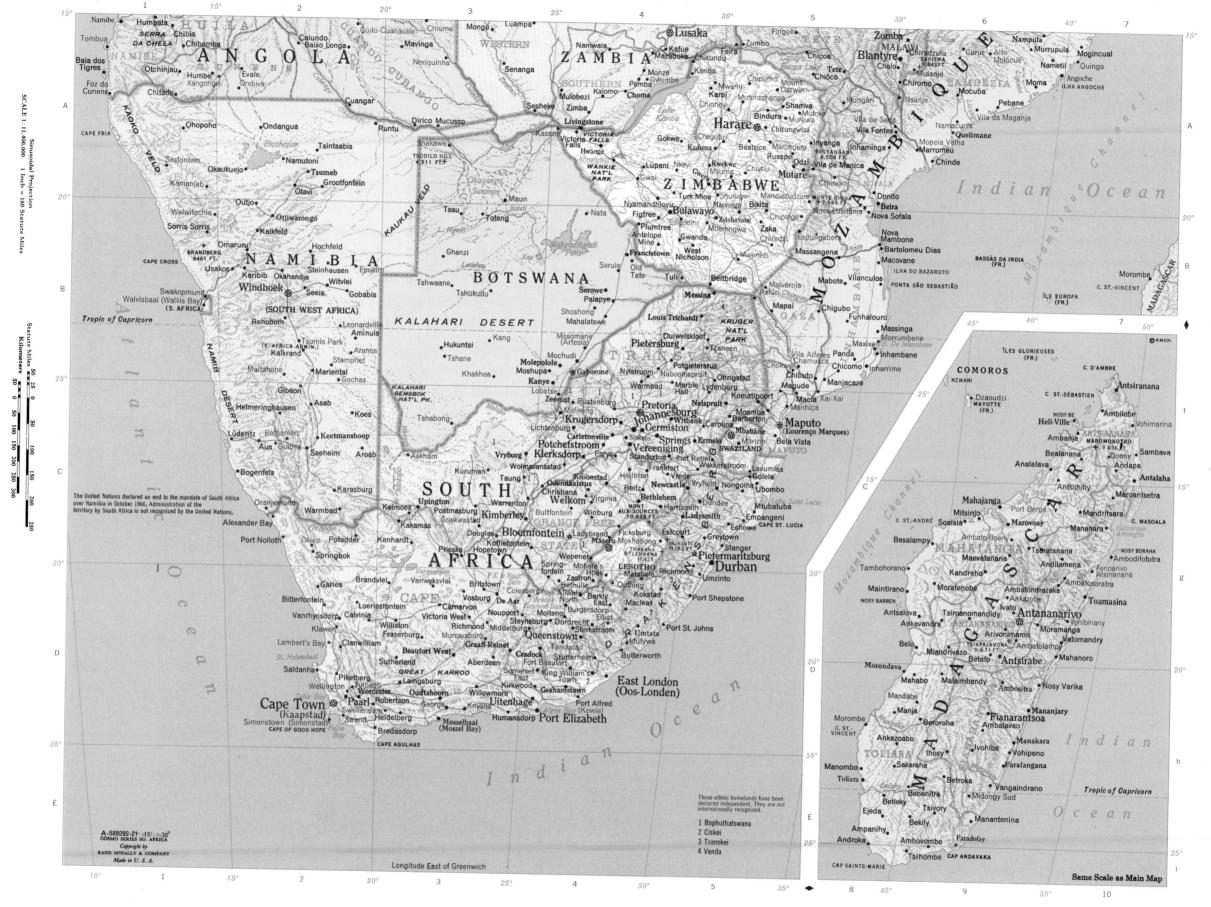

SOUTHERN AFRICA

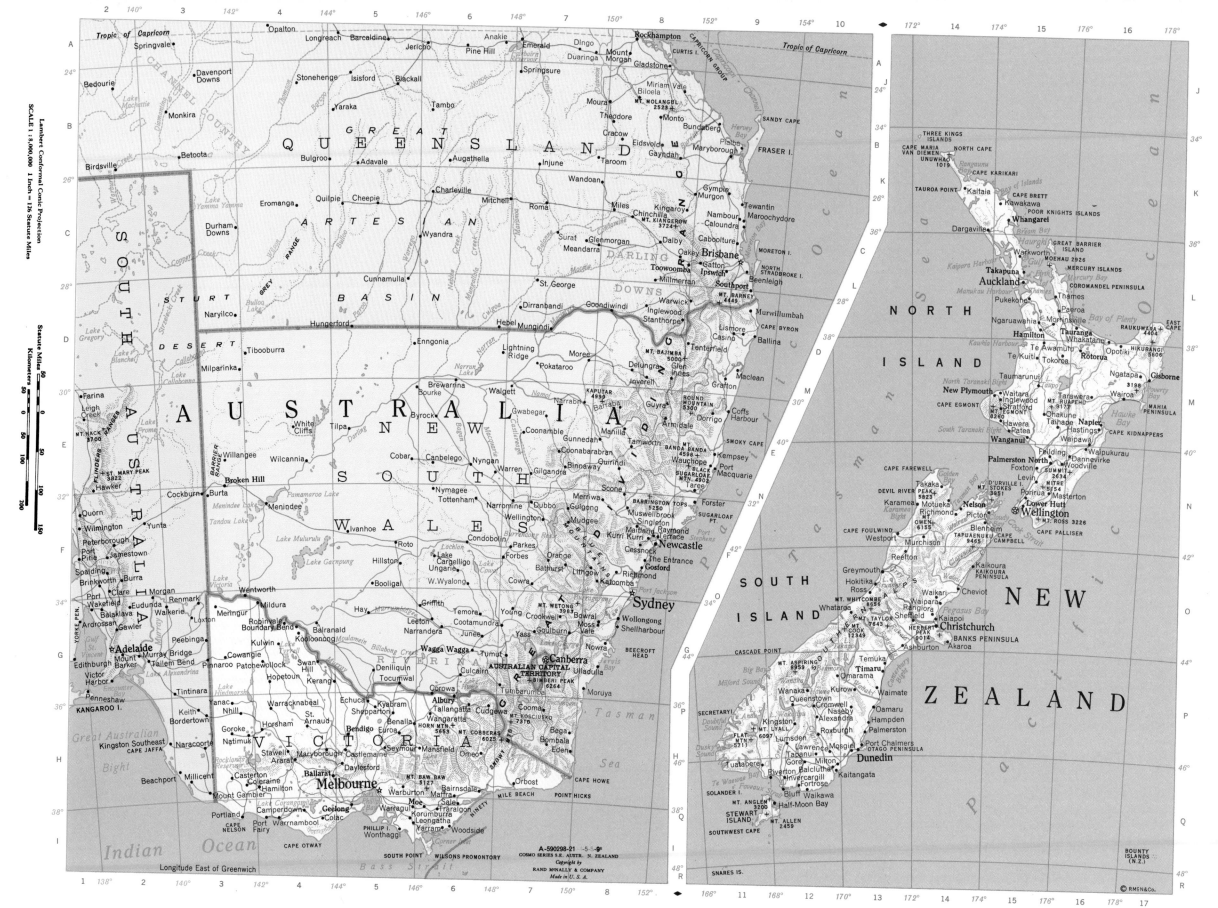

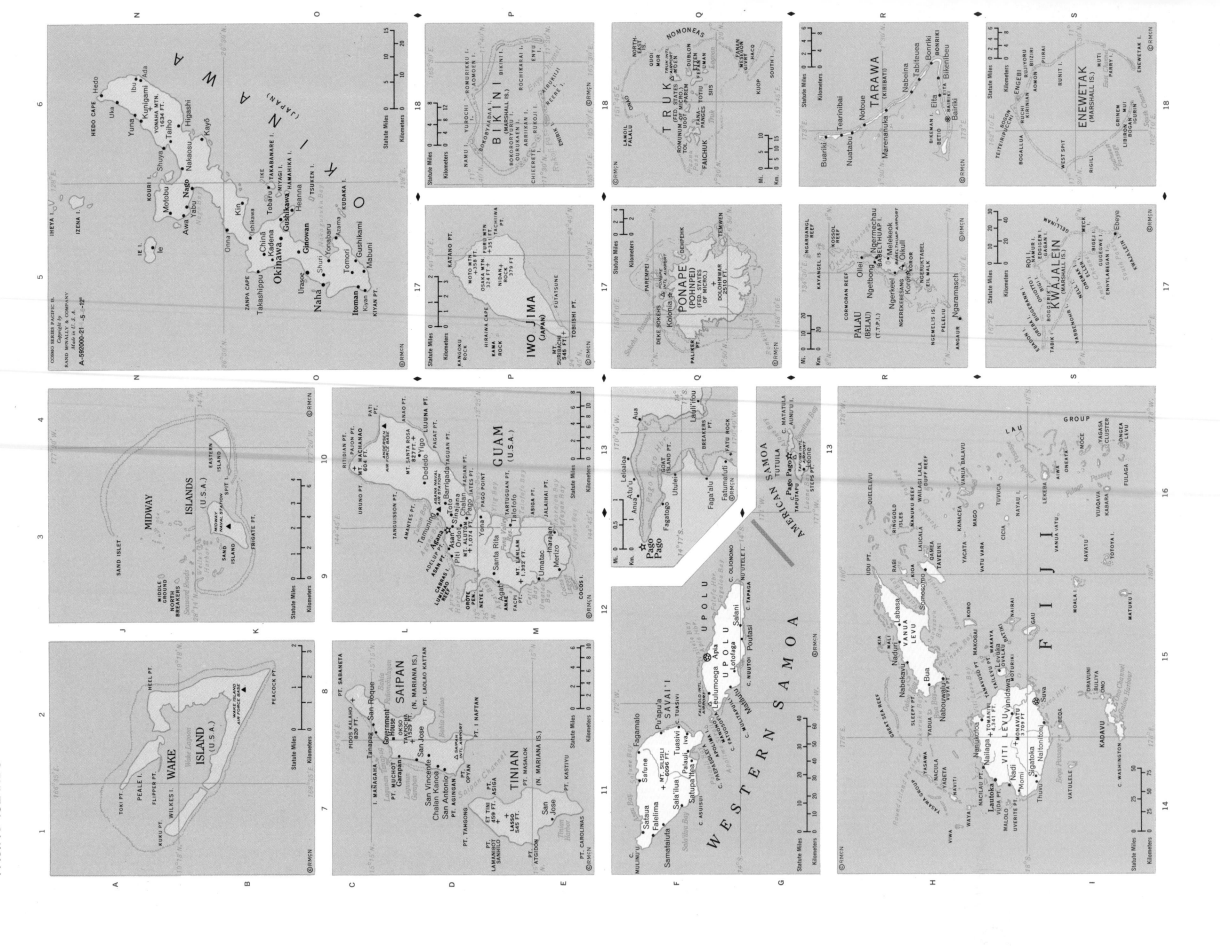

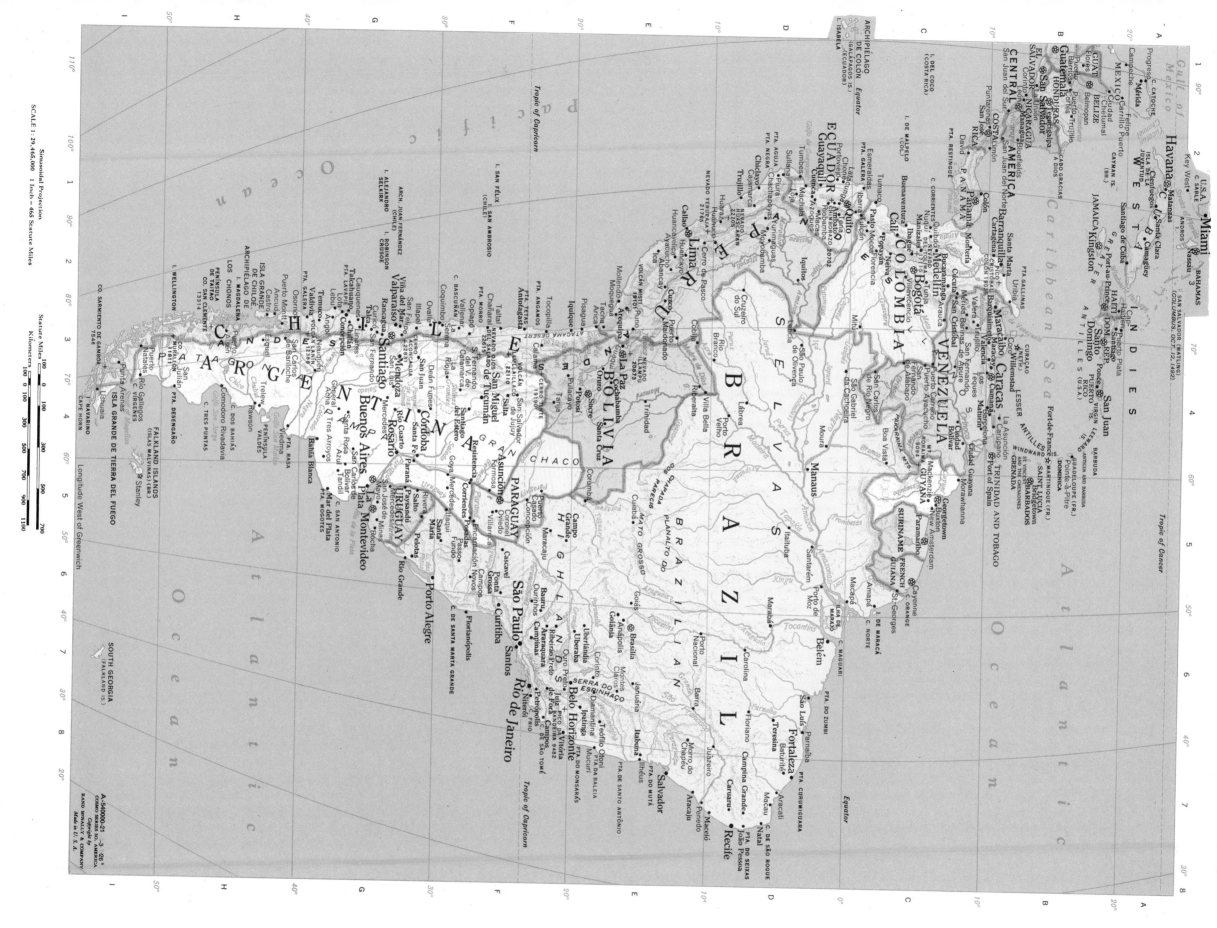

SOUTH AMERICA

SCALE 1: 29,465,000   1 Inch = 465 Statute Miles

Sinusoidal Projection

A-540000-21 -3-'26."
COSMO SERIES 5G, AMERICA
Copyright by
RAND M?NALLY & COMPANY
Made in U. S. A.

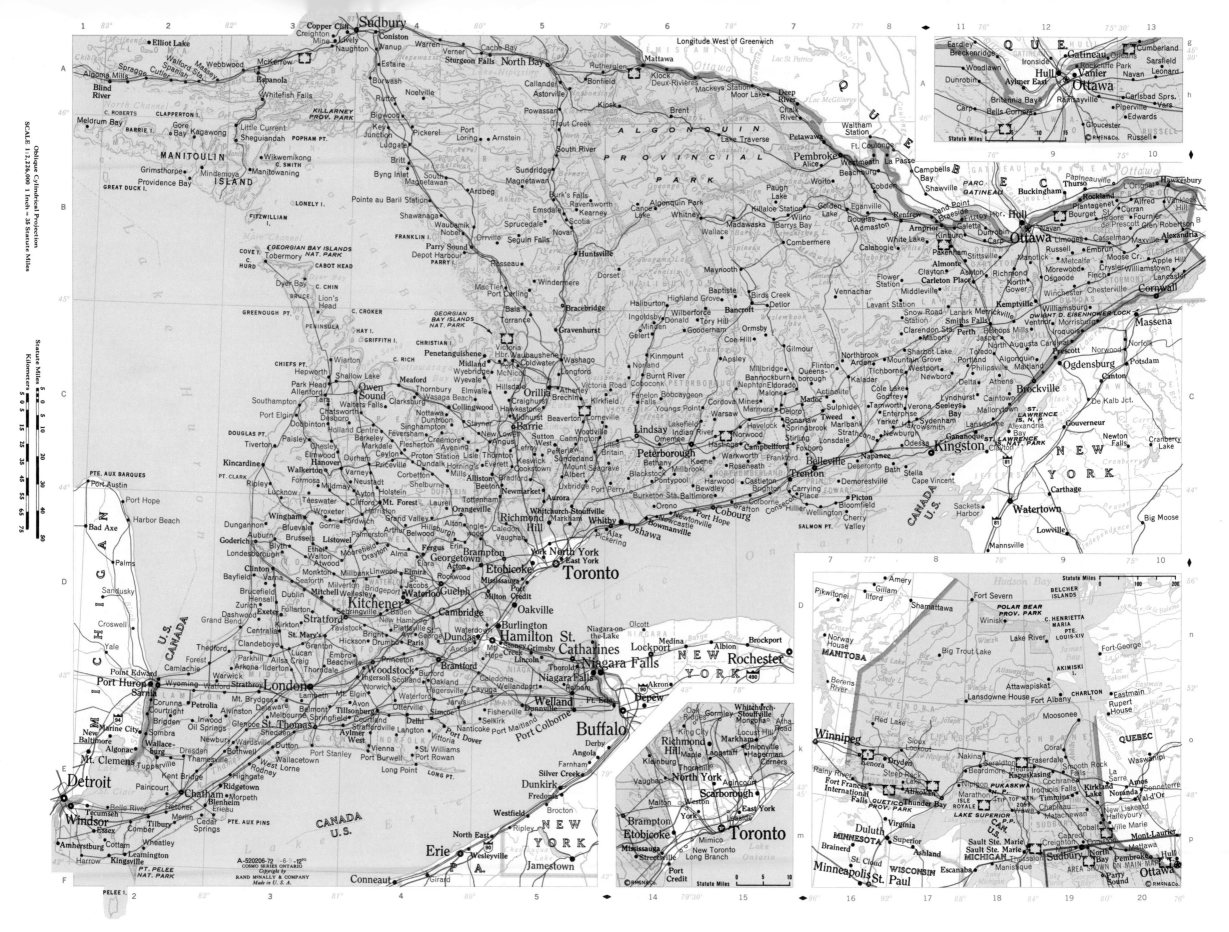

ONTARIO

73

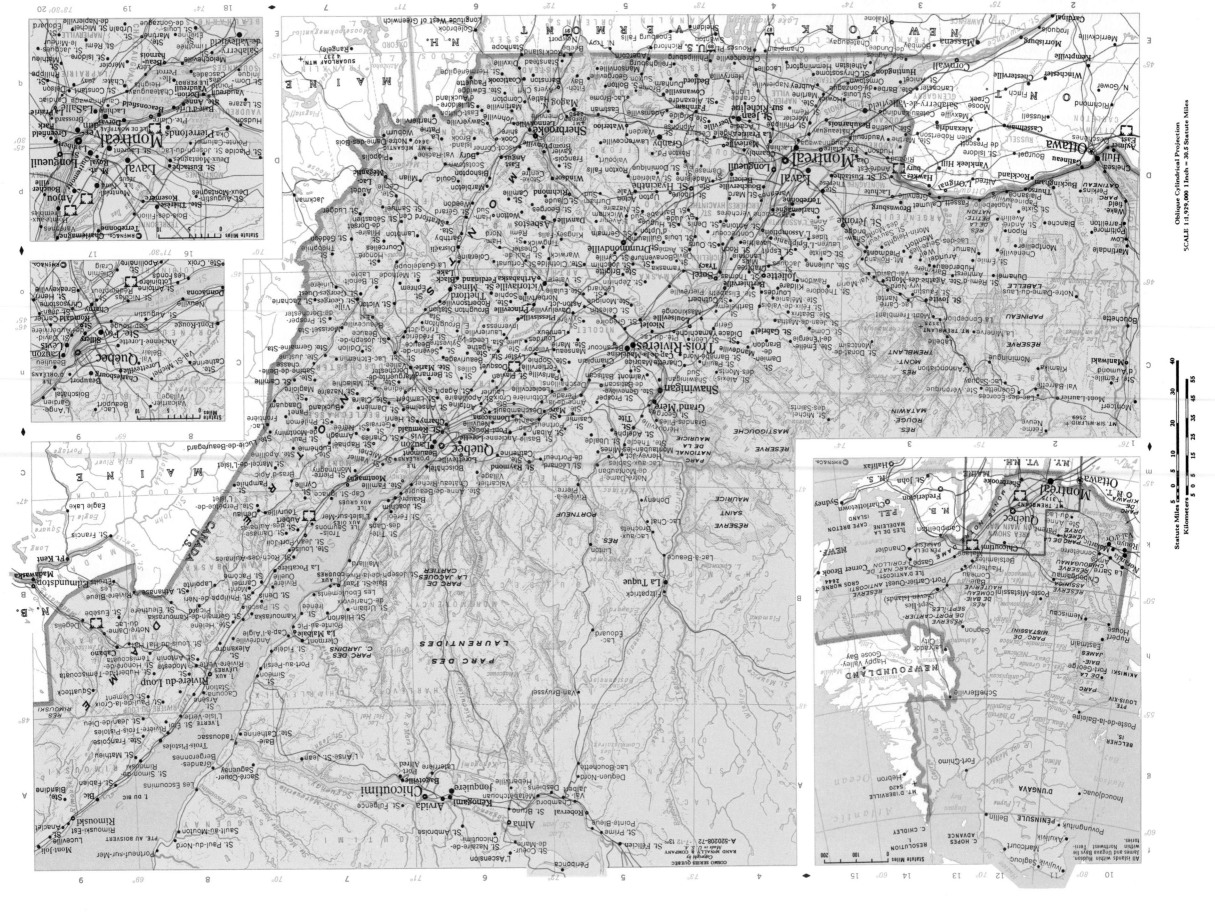

SCALE 1:1,929,000 1 Inch = 30.5 Statute Miles

Oblique Cylindrical Projection

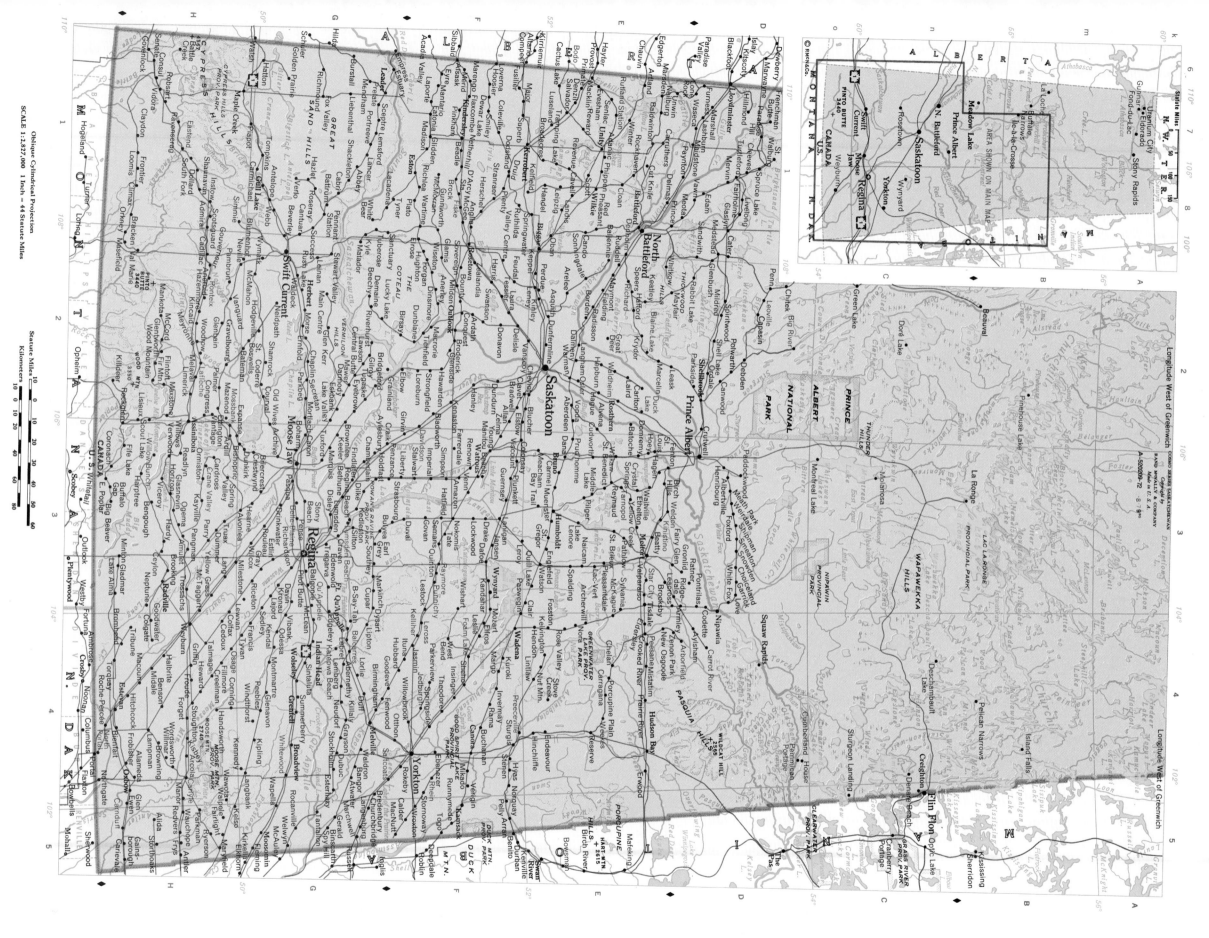

SASKATCHEWAN

Oblique Cylindrical Projection
SCALE 1:2,827,000   1 Inch = 44 Statute Miles

75

UNITED STATES OF AMERICA

Lambert Conformal Conic Projection
SCALE 1:12,000,000   1 Inch = 189 Statute Miles
Longitude West of Greenwich

MEXICO
YUCATAN
QUINTANA ROO
Mérida

Tropic of Cancer

Gulf of Mexico

Havana
Pinar del Río
Guane
Cárdenas
Matanzas
Cienfuegos
Santa Clara
Morón
Júcaro
Camagüey
Manzanillo
Gibara
Holguín
San Luis
Santiago de Cuba
Guantánamo
Baracoa
CUBA

ISLA DE LA JUVENTUD
SA. MAESTRA
C. CRUZ

HAITI
DOMINICAN REP.
Cap Haïtien
Santiago
Puerto Plata

BAHAMA ISLANDS
NEW PROVIDENCE
Nassau
ANDROS
ELEUTHERA I.
CAT I.
SAN SALVADOR
COLUMBUS, OCT. 12, 1492
LONG I.
GREAT EXUMA I.
CROOKED I.
ACKLINS I.
MAYAGUANA I.
GREAT INAGUA I.
CAICOS (BR.)

FLORIDA
Miami
Ft. Lauderdale
West Palm Beach
Key West
FLORIDA KEYS
Ft. Myers
St. Petersburg
Tampa
Clearwater
Sarasota
Lakeland
Orlando
Gainesville
Jacksonville
St. Augustine
Daytona Beach
EVERGLADES NAT'L PARK
CAPE CANAVERAL
C. SABLE
CAPE ROMANO

GEORGIA
Savannah
Brunswick
Columbus
Macon
Albany
Valdosta
Thomasville
Fitzgerald
Waycross
Augusta
CUMBERLAND I.

ALABAMA
Montgomery
Birmingham
Mobile
Dothan
Selma
Tuscaloosa
Gadsden
Talladega

MISSISSIPPI
Jackson
Meridian
Hattiesburg
Laurel
Gulfport
Biloxi
Natchez
Greenville
Clarksdale
Greenwood
Yazoo City

LOUISIANA
New Orleans
Baton Rouge
Shreveport
Monroe
Alexandria
Lafayette
Lake Charles
Gretna
Opelousas
Houma

ARKANSAS
Little Rock
Fort Smith
Pine Bluff
Hot Springs
Texarkana
Jonesboro
El Dorado
Camden

TENNESSEE
Nashville
Memphis
Chattanooga
Knoxville
Jackson

KENTUCKY
Louisville
Lexington
Frankfort
Owensboro
Bowling Green
Paducah

NORTH CAROLINA
Charlotte
Raleigh
Durham
Greensboro
Winston-Salem
Wilmington
Fayetteville
Asheville
Rocky Mount
New Bern
CAPE HATTERAS
CAPE LOOKOUT
C. FEAR

S. CAROLINA
Columbia
Charleston
Georgetown
Florence
Greenville
Spartanburg
C. ROMAIN

VIRGINIA
Richmond
Norfolk
Roanoke
Lynchburg
Petersburg
Newport News
Danville
C. CHARLES
C. HENRY

W. VIRGINIA
Charleston
Huntington
Parkersburg
Wheeling
Clarksburg

OHIO
Columbus
Cincinnati
Cleveland
Dayton
Toledo
Akron
Chillicothe
Springfield

INDIANA
Indianapolis
Ft. Wayne
South Bend
Evansville
Terre Haute
Bloomington

ILLINOIS
Chicago
Springfield
Peoria
Decatur
Champaign
Quincy
Mattoon

MICHIGAN
Detroit
Grand Rapids
Lansing
Saginaw
Flint
Kalamazoo
Muskegon
Traverse City
Cadillac
Alpena
Marquette
Escanaba
Houghton
Sault Ste. Marie
ISLE ROYALE (NAT'L PK.)
MANITOULIN I.

WISCONSIN
Milwaukee
Madison
Green Bay
Racine
Kenosha
Oshkosh
Appleton
Sheboygan
Manitowoc
Duluth

MINNESOTA
Minneapolis
St. Paul
Rochester

IOWA
Cedar Rapids
Dubuque
Davenport
Waterloo
Mason City

MISSOURI
St. Louis
Columbia
Moberly
Hannibal

PENNSYLVANIA
Pittsburgh
Philadelphia
Harrisburg
Scranton
Allentown
Johnstown
Altoona
Williamsport
Wilkes-Barre
Reading

NEW YORK
New York
Buffalo
Rochester
Syracuse
Albany
Utica
Binghamton
Watertown
Yonkers
LONG ISLAND

NEW JERSEY
Newark
Trenton
Atlantic City
C. MAY

MARYLAND
Baltimore
Washington, D.C.
Annapolis
Salisbury

DELAWARE
Wilmington
Dover

CONNECTICUT
Hartford
Bridgeport
New Haven

RHODE ISLAND
Providence

MASSACHUSETTS
Boston
Worcester
Springfield
Lowell
Lawrence
New Bedford
Lynn

N.H.
Manchester
Portsmouth

VERMONT

MAINE
Portland
Augusta
Bangor
Calais
Houlton
Caribou
Presque Isle
MT. KATAHDIN 5268
C. SABLE

Atlantic Ocean

BERMUDA IS. (BR.)

CANADA

QUEBEC
Montreal
Quebec
Ottawa
Hull
Trois-Rivières
Sherbrooke
Chicoutimi
Chibougamau
MONT TREMBLANT PARK
ALGONQUIN PARK
LAURENTIDES PARK
NOTRE DAME MTS.
GREEN MTS.
WHITE MTS.
ILE D'ANTICOSTI
Gaspé
Gulf of St. Lawrence
MAGDALEN IS. (QUEBEC)

ONTARIO
Toronto
Hamilton
London
Kitchener
Windsor
Sudbury
North Bay
Timmins
Cochrane
Hearst
Kingston
Peterborough
Owen Sound
Parry Sound
Thunder Bay
QUETICO PROVINCIAL PARK
AKIMISKI I.
Moosonee
Albany
Rupert House
Ft. Albany

NEW BRUNSWICK
Fredericton
Saint John
Moncton
Edmundston

NOVA SCOTIA
Halifax
Dartmouth
Yarmouth
Sydney
Glace Bay
New Glasgow
Amherst
CAPE BRETON I.
NAT'L PARK
CAPE BRETON
C. CANSO
C. NORTH

PRINCE EDWARD ISLAND
Charlottetown

NEWFOUNDLAND
Channel-Port aux Basques
MT. JACQUES CARTIER 4160

Lake Superior
Lake Michigan
Lake Huron
Lake Erie
Lake Ontario

77

ALABAMA

78

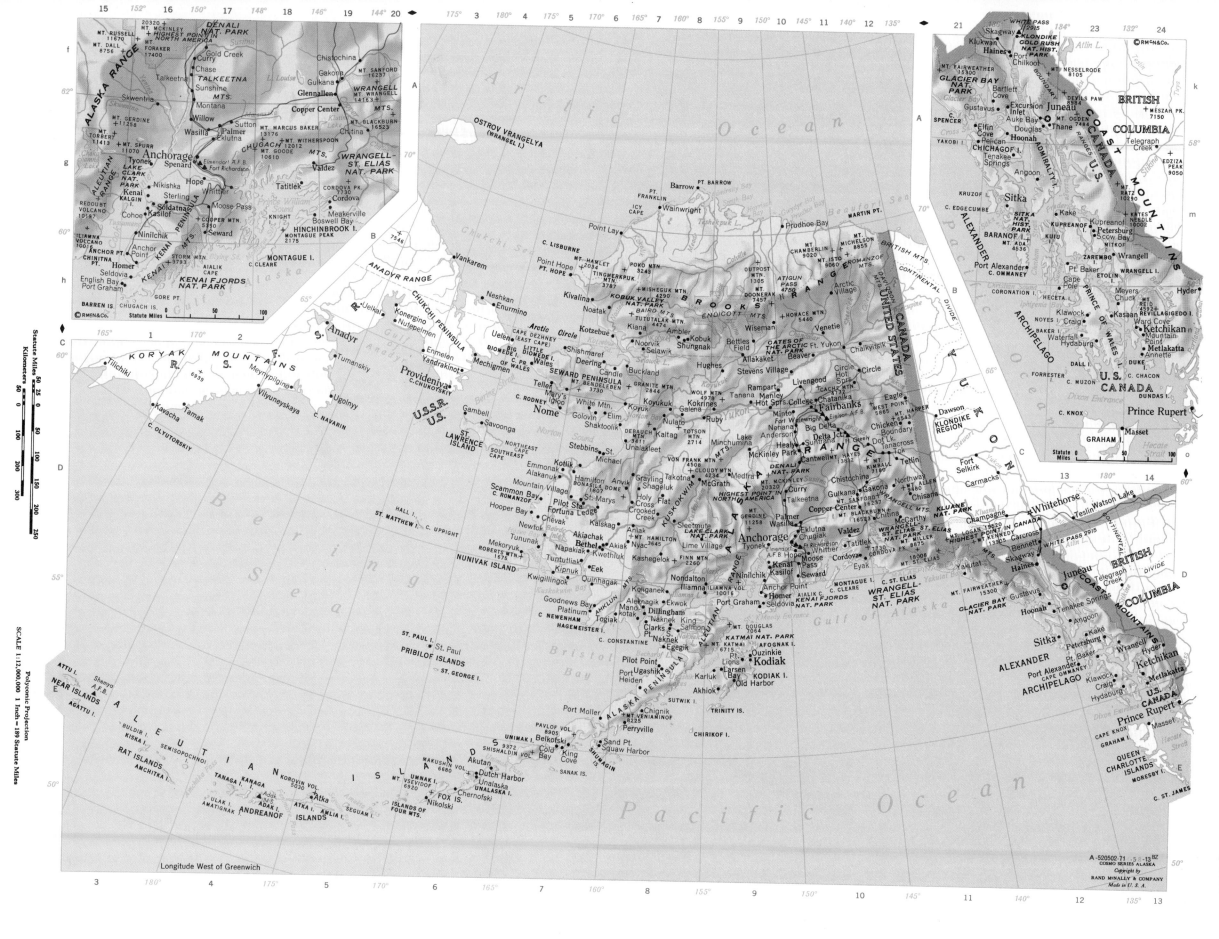

ALASKA

A-520502-71 · 5 · -13 BZ
COSMO SERIES ALASKA
Copyright by
RAND M°NALLY & COMPANY
Made in U.S.A.

SCALE 1:12,000,000 1 Inch = 189 Statute Miles
Polyconic Projection

Longitude West of Greenwich

ARIZONA

80

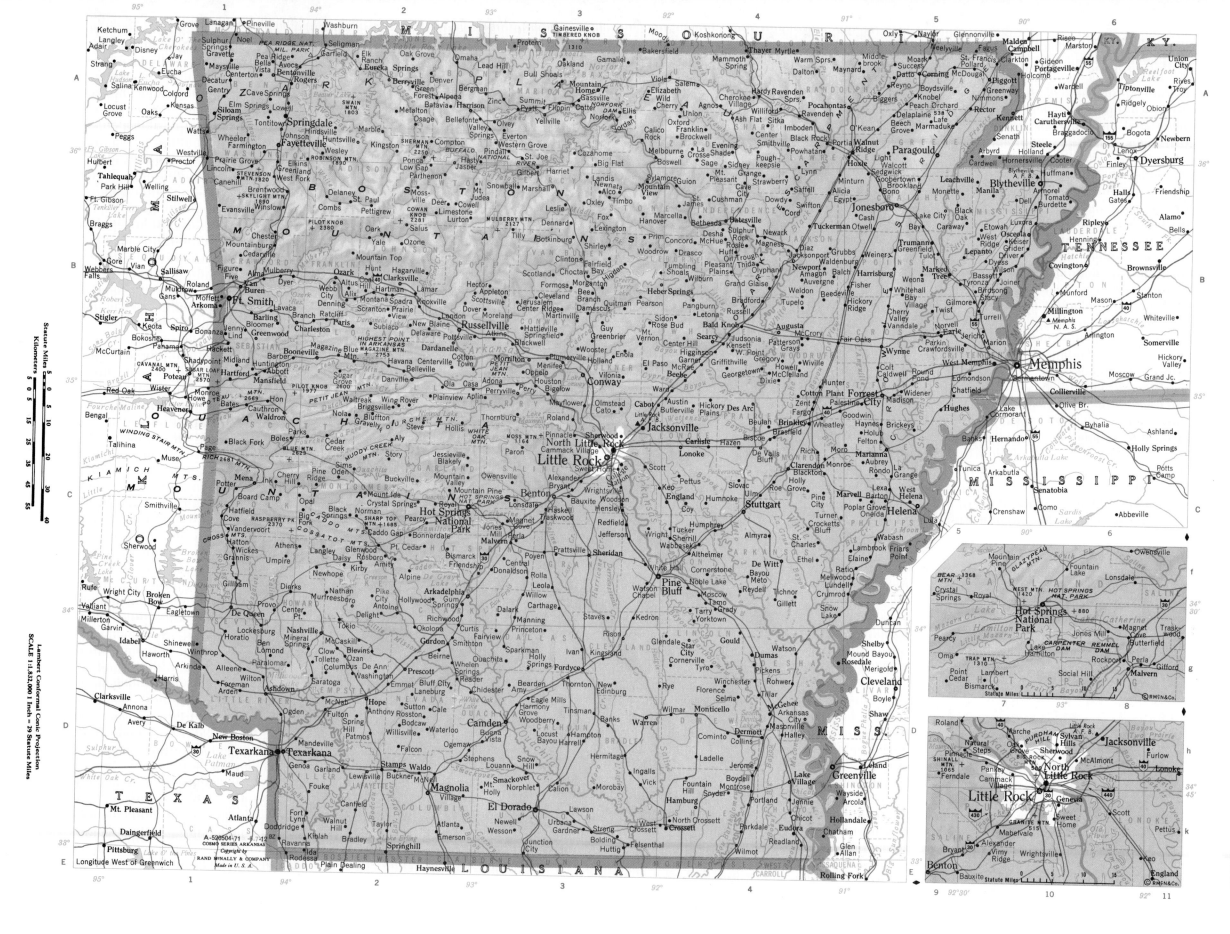

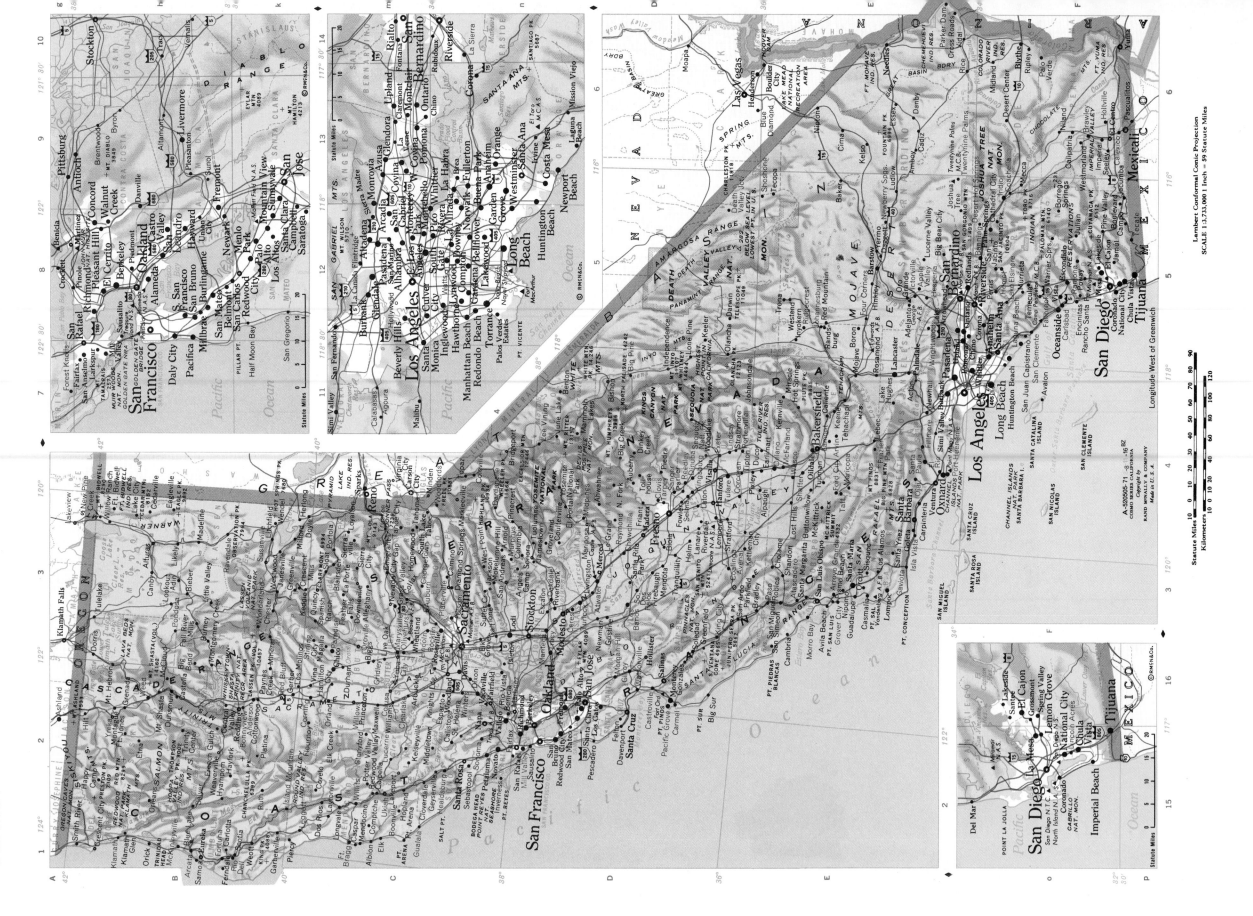

CALIFORNIA

82

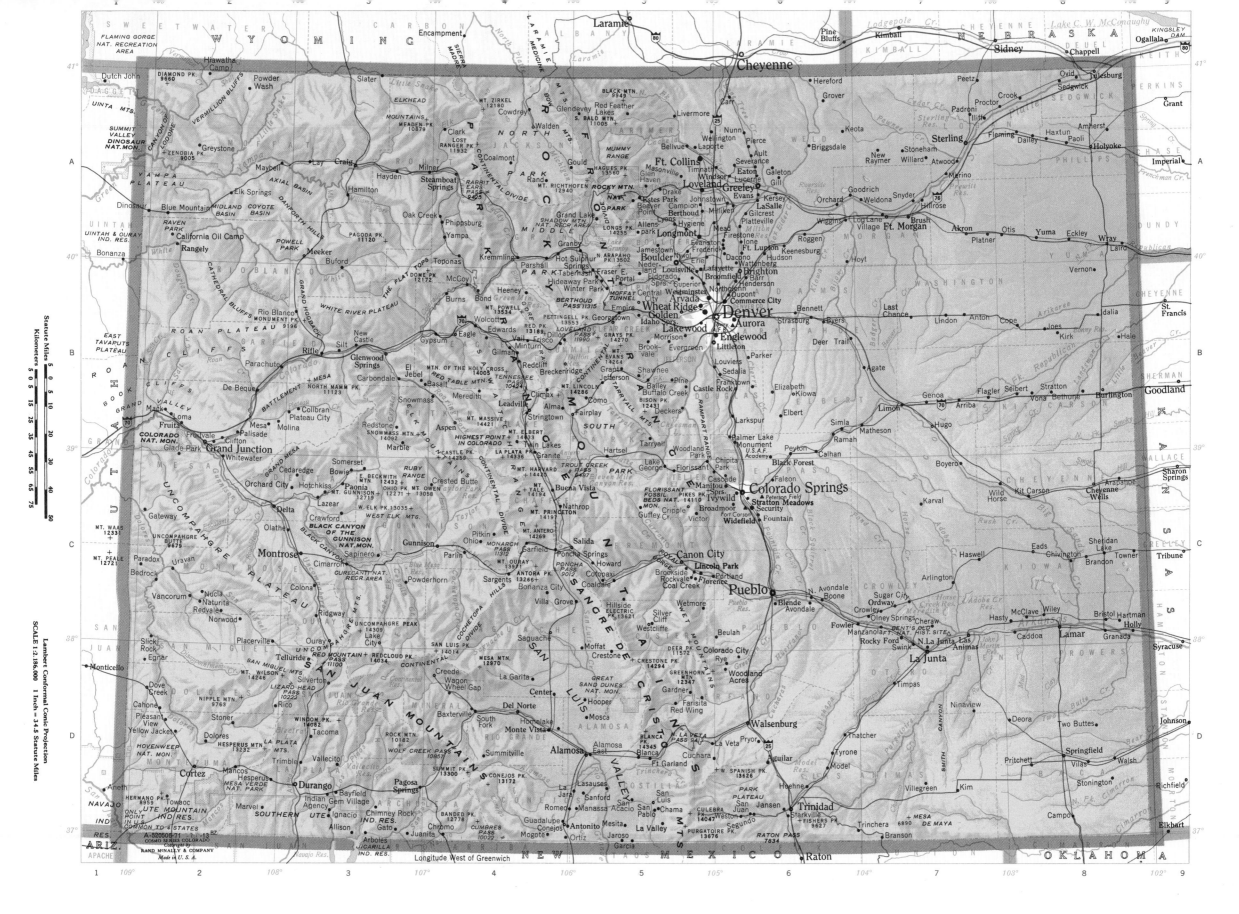

Lambert Conformal Conic Projection
SCALE 1:2,186,000   1 Inch = 34.5 Statute Miles

Statute Miles

Kilometers

A-520506-71 313
COSMO SERIES COLORADO
Copyright by
RAND M?NALLY & COMPANY
Made in U.S.A.

CONNECTICUT

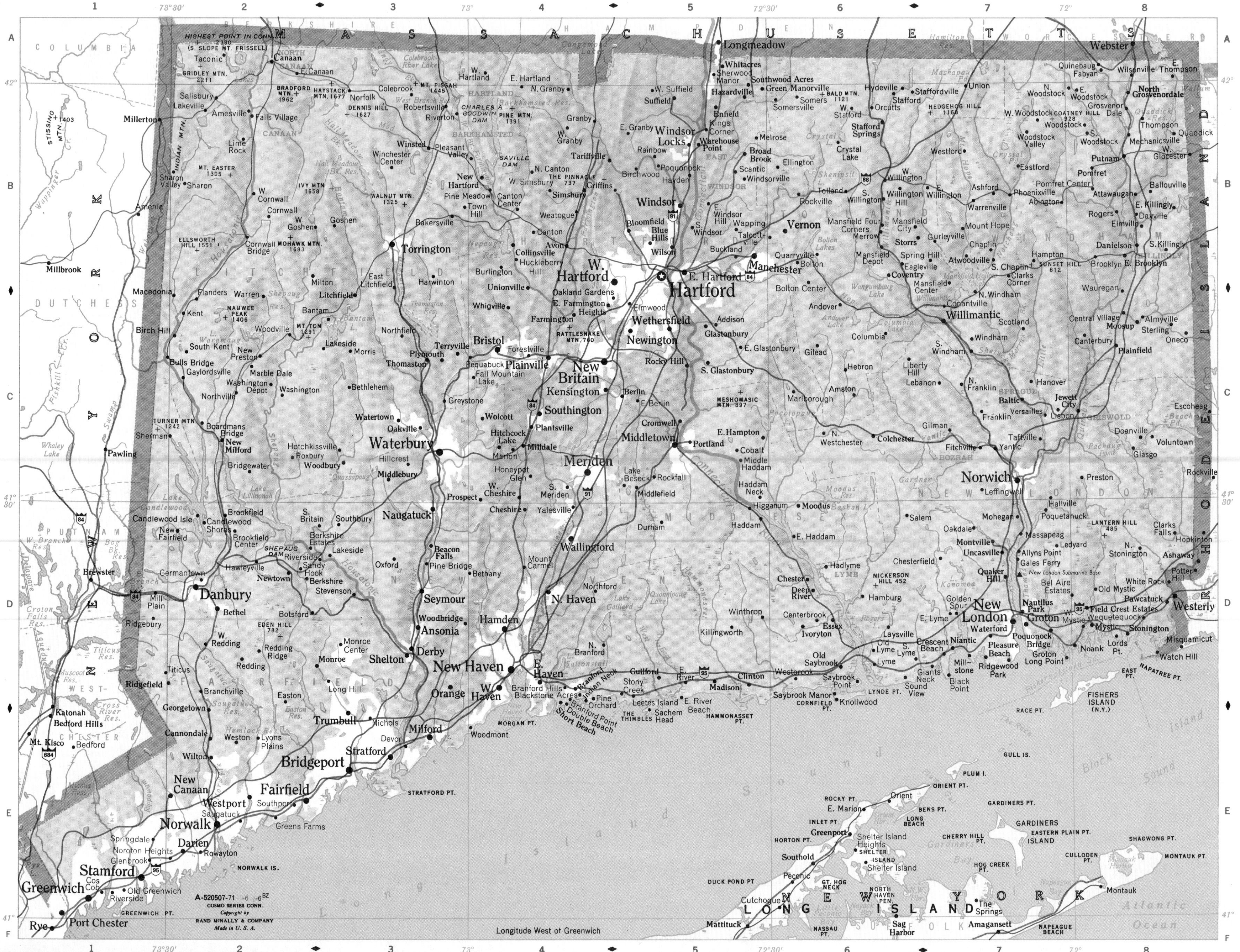

Lambert Conformal Conic Projection
SCALE 1:545,000 1 Inch = 8.6 Statute Miles

Copyright by
RAND M~NALLY & COMPANY
COSMO SERIES CONN.
Made in U.S.A.
A-520507-71—6—6-82

Longitude West of Greenwich

Statute Miles
Kilometers

NEW YORK

MASSACHUSETTS

RHODE ISLAND

Atlantic Ocean

Long Island Sound

Block Island Sound

LONG ISLAND, N.Y.

Hartford
New Haven
Bridgeport
Stamford
Norwalk
Danbury
Waterbury
New Britain
Meriden
Middletown
New London
Norwich
Willimantic
Manchester
East Hartford
West Hartford
Torrington
Fairfield
Westport
Milford
Stratford
Shelton
Derby
Ansonia
Naugatuck
Hamden
Branford
Guilford
Clinton
Madison
Westbrook
Old Saybrook
Essex
Groton
Mystic
Stonington
Westerly
Putnam
Danielson

84

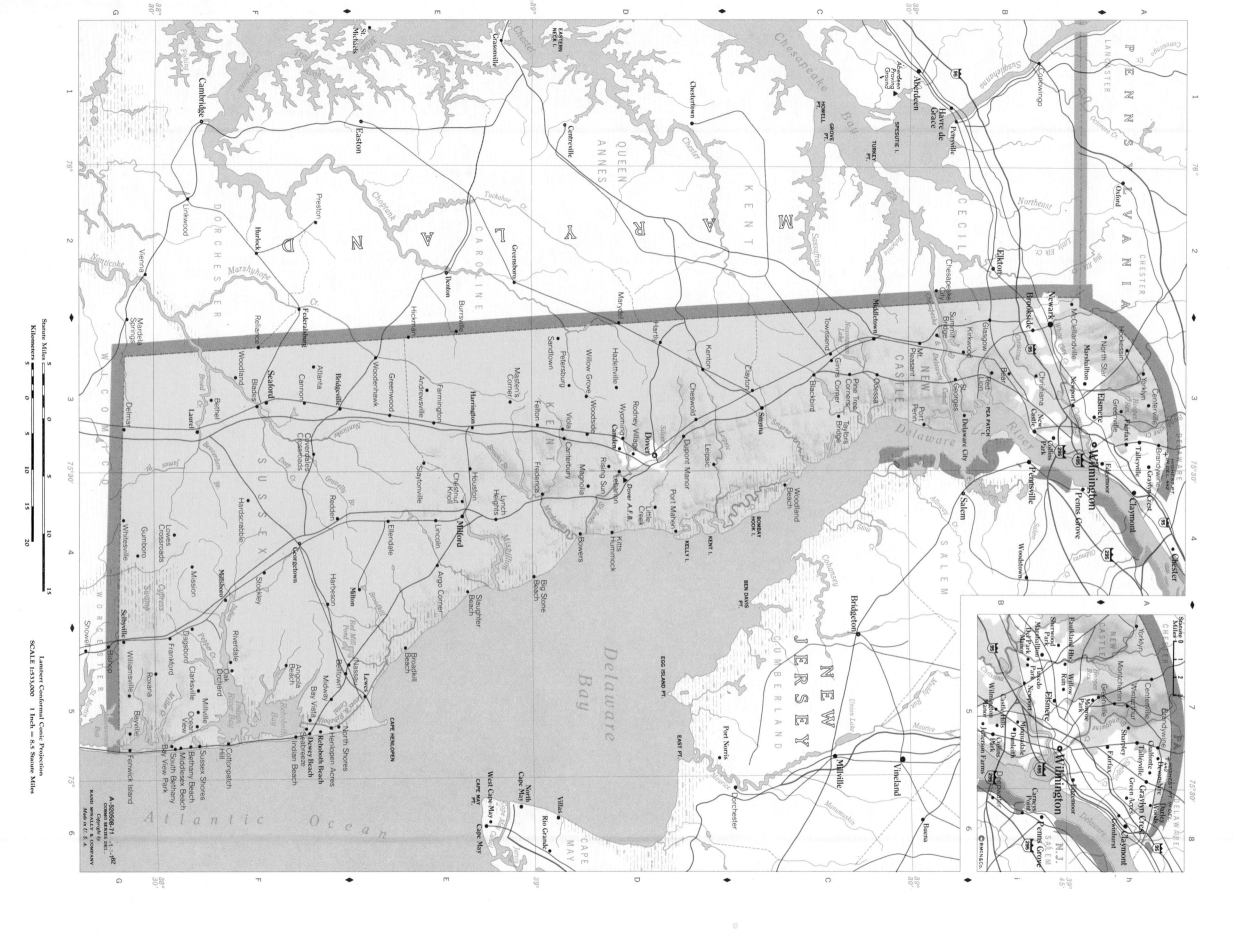

DELAWARE

85

Lambert Conformal Conic Projection
SCALE 1:533,000   1 Inch = 8.5 Statute Miles

A-520508-71   11   82
OSMO SERIES DEL.
Copyright by
RAND McNALLY & COMPANY
Made in U.S.A.

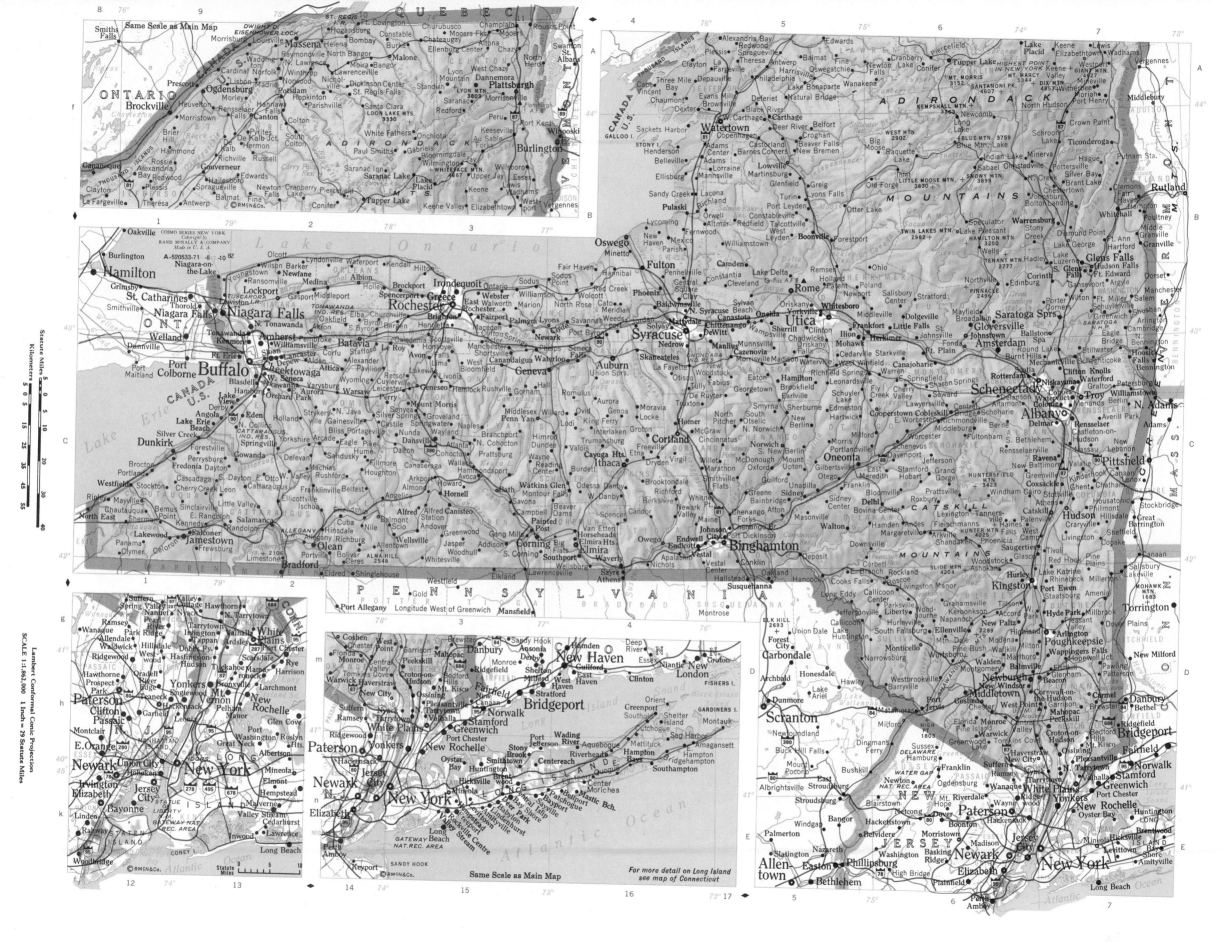

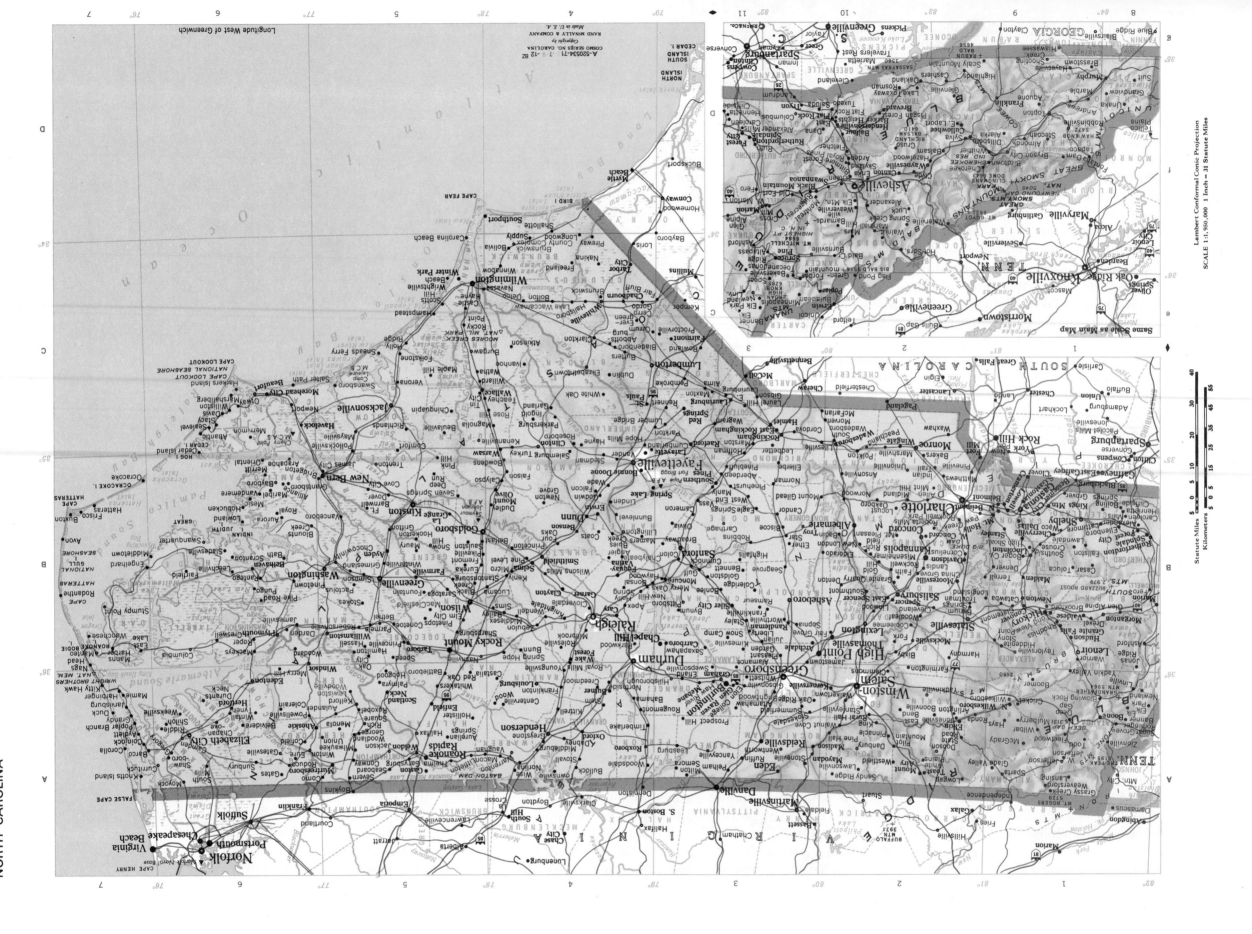

NORTH CAROLINA

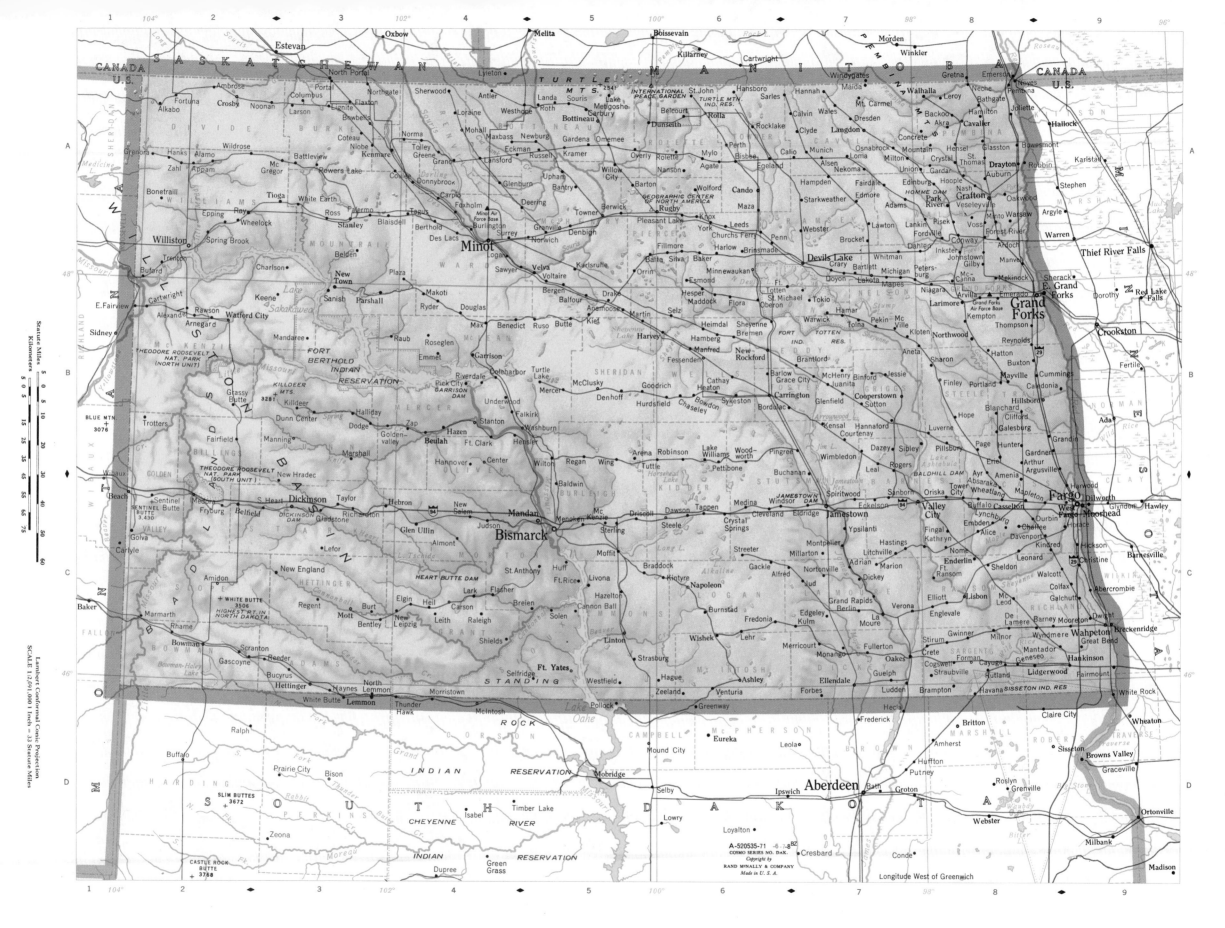

NORTH DAKOTA

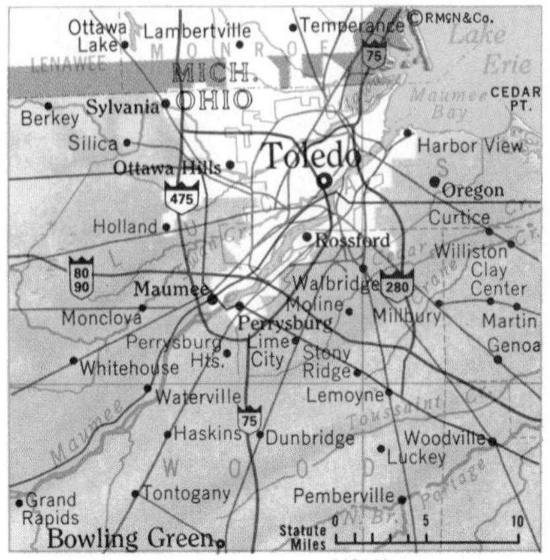

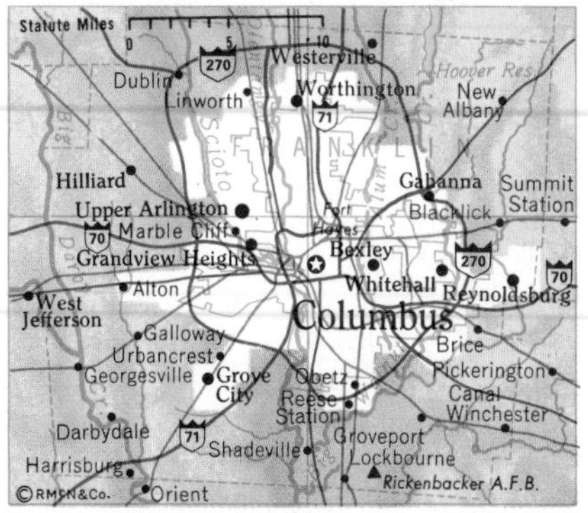

OHIO

Lambert Conformal Conic Projection
SCALE 1:1,714,000 1 Inch = 27 Statute Miles

Longitude West of Greenwich

Cincinnati

Hamilton

Columbus

Cleveland

Toledo

Index

Name	Map Ref	Page

Index

Index

Index

Name	Map Ref	Page

142

148

Name	Map Ref	Page

Index

Index

Name	Map Ref	Page
Fithian, Il., U.S.	C6	90
Filer, Ms., U.S.	C2	101
Fittstown, Ok., U.S.	C5	113
Fitzgerald, Ga., U.S.	E3	87
Fitzroy, Ok., U.S.	C5	113
Fitzpatrick, P.Q., Can.	D4	69
Fitz Roy, Arg.	B5	74
Fitzroy, stm., Austl.	D9	54
Fitzroy, stm., Austl.	D9	50
Fitzroy, Monte (Cerro Chaltel), mtn., S.A.	D2	54
Fitzroy Harbour, Nf. Can.	E2	106
Fitzwilliam, N.H., U.S.	E2	106
Fitzwilliam Depot, N.H., U.S.	B3	73
Fitzwilliam Island, i., On., Can.	A3	78
Fiume Veneto, Italy		
Fivemiletown, N. Ire., U.K.	G12	9
Five Island Lake, l., N.S., Can.	H2	71
Five Points, Al., U.S.		
Five Points, N.M., U.S.		
Fiumicine Creek, stm., Wy.		
Fizi, Zaire	C4	127
Fjärdhundra, Swe.	B4	78
Fjerritslev, Den.	E7	114

(Back-of-book atlas index — Names with Map Reference and Page columns. Entries continue across multiple columns covering "Fith" through "Fountain Peak", including Fleur-de-Lys, Flagler, Flaming Gorge, Flathead, Flensburg, Fletcher, Florence, Florida, Foam Lake, Folsom, Fond du Lac, Fonseca, Fontana, Forsyth, Fort (numerous), Fortune, Fossil, Foster, Fostoria, and Fountain series.)

Index

Name	Map Ref	Page
Jasper, In., U.S.	H4	91
Jasper, Mn., U.S.	G2	100
Jasper, Mo., U.S.	D3	102
Jasper, N.Y., U.S.	C3	109
Jasper, Oh., U.S.	C2	112
Jasper, Or., U.S.	D4	114
Jasper, Tn., U.S.	D8	119
Jasper, Tx., U.S.	D6	120
Jasper, co., Ga., U.S.	C3	87
Jasper, co., Il., U.S.	D5	90
Jasper, co., In., U.S.	B3	91
Jasper, co., Ia., U.S.	C4	92
Jasper, co., Ms., U.S.	C4	101
Jasper, co., Mo., U.S.	D3	102
Jasper, co., S.C., U.S.	G5	117
Jasper, co., Tx., U.S.	D5	120
Jasper Lake, l., Ab., Can.	C1	68
Jasper National Park, Ab., Can.	C1	68
Jastarnia, Pol.	A5	26
Jastrzebia Góra, Pol.	A5	26
Jastrzębie-Zdrój, Pol.	h9	26
Jászapáti, Hung.	B5	24
Jászberény, Hung.	B4	24
Jataí, Braz.	B2	56
Jāti, Pak.	E2	37
Jatibonico, Cuba	D4	64
Játiva, Spain	C5	22
Jatni, India	G10	37
Jatobá, stm., Braz.	E4	59
Jaú, Braz.	C3	56
Jaú, stm., Braz.	C2	59
Jauaperi, stm., Braz.	B2	59
Jaumave, Mex.	C5	63
Jaunpur, India	C7	36
Java, S.D., U.S.	B6	118
Java, Va., U.S.	D3	123
Java (Jawa), i., Indon.	G3	34
Javari see Yavarí, stm., S.A.	B3	58
Java Sea, Indon.	G4	34
Jávea, Spain	C6	22
Jawhār, India	H4	37
Jawor, Pol.	C4	26
Jaworzno, Pol.	g10	26
Jay, Fl., U.S.	u14	86
Jay, La., U.S.	E5	95
Jay, Me., U.S.	D2	96
Jay, N.Y., U.S.	f11	109
Jay, Ok., U.S.	A7	113
Jay, co., In., U.S.	D7	91
Jayanca, Peru	C2	58
Jaya Peak, mtn., Indon.	F9	34
Jayapura (Sukarnapura), Indon.	F10	34
Jay Em, Wy., U.S.	D8	127
Jayess, Ms., U.S.	D3	101
Jay Peak, mtn., Vt., U.S.	B3	122
Jayton, Tx., U.S.	C2	120
Jaz Mūrīān, Hāmūn-e, l., Iran	H9	39
J. B. Thomas, Lake, res., Tx., U.S.	C2	120
Jean, Nv., U.S.	H6	105
Jeanerette, La., U.S.	E4	95
Jean Lafitte National Historical Park, La., U.S.	k12	95
Jeannette, Pa., U.S.	F2	115
Jeannette Island, i., Sov. Un.	B35	128
Jebba, Nig.	E5	45
Jeberos, Peru	C2	58
Jedburg, S.C., U.S.	h11	117
Jedburgh, Sk., Can.	F4	75
Jedburgh, Scot., U.K.	C5	10
Jeddito, Az., U.S.	B5	80
Jeddo, Mi., U.S.	E8	99
Jeddore Lake, res., Nf., Can.	D3	72
Jędrzejów, Pol.	C6	26
Jeetze, stm., Eur.	B5	18
Jeff, Ky., U.S.	C6	94
Jeff Davis, co., Ga., U.S.	E4	87
Jeff Davis, co., Tx., U.S.	o12	120
Jeffers, Mn., U.S.	F3	100
Jeffers, Mt., U.S.	E5	103
Jefferson, Al., U.S.	C2	78
Jefferson, Ar., U.S.	C3	81
Jefferson, Co., U.S.	B5	83
Jefferson, Ga., U.S.	B3	87
Jefferson, In., U.S.	D4	91
Jefferson, Ia., U.S.	B3	92
Jefferson, La., U.S.	k11	95
Jefferson, Me., U.S.	D3	96
Jefferson, Md., U.S.	B2	97
Jefferson, Ma., U.S.	B4	98
Jefferson, N.H., U.S.	B4	106
Jefferson, N.J., U.S.	D2	107
Jefferson, N.Y., U.S.	C6	109
Jefferson, N.C., U.S.	A1	110
Jefferson, Oh., U.S.	A5	112
Jefferson, Ok., U.S.	A4	113
Jefferson, Or., U.S.	C3	114
Jefferson, Pa., U.S.	*F2	115
Jefferson, S.C., U.S.	B7	117
Jefferson, S.D., U.S.	E9	118
Jefferson, Tx., U.S.	C5	120
Jefferson, Wi., U.S.	E5	126
Jefferson, co., Al., U.S.	B3	78
Jefferson, co., Ar., U.S.	C3	81
Jefferson, co., Co., U.S.	B5	83
Jefferson, co., Fl., U.S.	B3	86
Jefferson, co., Ga., U.S.	C4	87
Jefferson, co., Id., U.S.	F6	89
Jefferson, co., Il., U.S.	E5	90
Jefferson, co., In., U.S.	G6	91
Jefferson, co., Ia., U.S.	C5	92
Jefferson, co., Ks., U.S.	C8	93
Jefferson, co., Ky., U.S.	B4	94
Jefferson, co., La., U.S.	E5	95
Jefferson, co., Ms., U.S.	D2	101
Jefferson, co., Mo., U.S.	C7	102
Jefferson, co., Mt., U.S.	D4	103
Jefferson, co., Ne., U.S.	D8	104
Jefferson, co., N.Y., U.S.	A5	109
Jefferson, co., Oh., U.S.	B5	112
Jefferson, co., Ok., U.S.	C4	113
Jefferson, co., Or., U.S.	C5	114
Jefferson, co., Pa., U.S.	D3	115
Jefferson, co., Tn., U.S.	C10	119
Jefferson, co., Tx., U.S.	E5	120
Jefferson, co., Wa., U.S.	B2	124
Jefferson, co., W.V., U.S.	B7	125
Jefferson, co., Wi., U.S.	E5	126
Jefferson, stm., Mt., U.S.	E5	103
Jefferson, Mount, mtn., Id., U.S.	E7	89
Jefferson, Mount, mtn., Nv., U.S.	E5	105
Jefferson, Mount, mtn., Or., U.S.	C5	114
Jefferson City, Mo., U.S.	C5	102
Jefferson City, Mt., U.S.	D5	103
Jefferson City, Tn., U.S.	C10	119
Jefferson Davis, co., La., U.S.	D3	95
Jefferson Davis, co., Ms., U.S.	D4	101
Jefferson Farms, De., U.S.	i7	85
Jefferson Hill, hill, Ky., U.S.	g11	94
Jefferson Manor, Va., U.S.	*B5	123
Jefferson Proving Ground, mil., In., U.S.	G7	91
Jeffersontown, Ky., U.S.	B4	94
Jefferson Village, Va., U.S.	*B5	123
Jeffersonville, Ga., U.S.	D3	87
Jeffersonville, In., U.S.	H6	91
Jeffersonville, Ky., U.S.	C6	94
Jeffersonville, N.Y., U.S.	D6	109
Jeffersonville, Oh., U.S.	C2	112
Jeffersonville, Vt., U.S.	B3	122
Jeffrey, W.V., U.S.	D3	125
Jeffrey City, Wy., U.S.	D5	127
Jeffries Creek, stm., S.C., U.S.	C8	117
Jega, Nig.	D5	45
Jehossee Island, i., S.C., U.S.	k11	117
Jejui-Guazú, stm., Para.	D4	55
Jēkabpils, Sov. Un.	C5	27
Jekyll Island, i., Ga., U.S.	E5	87
Jelenia Góra (Hirschberg), Pol.	C3	26
Jelgava (Yelgava), Sov. Un.	C4	27
Jellico, Tn., U.S.	C9	119
Jelling, Den.	C3	15
Jelm, Wy., U.S.	E6	127
Jelm Mountain, mtn., Wy., U.S.	E7	127
Jelöya, i., Nor.	p28	14
Jemaja, i., Indon.	K6	35
Jember, Indon.	G4	34
Jemez, stm., N.M., U.S.	k7	108
Jemez Dam, N.M., U.S.	k7	108
Jemez Indian Reservation, N.M., U.S.	h7	108
Jemez Pueblo, N.M., U.S.	B3	108
Jemez Springs, N.M., U.S.	B3	108
Jemison, Al., U.S.	C3	78
Jemseg, N.B., Can.	D3	71
Jemtland, Me., U.S.	A4	96
Jena, Ger.D.R.	C5	18
Jena, Fl., U.S.	C3	86
Jena, La., U.S.	C3	95
Jenaz, Switz.	C8	21
Jenbach, Aus.	B7	20
Jendouba, Tun.	F2	23
Jenera, Oh., U.S.	B2	112
Jenison, Mi., U.S.	*F5	99
Jenkins, Ky., U.S.	C7	94
Jenkins, Mn., U.S.	D4	100
Jenkins, N.J., U.S.	D3	107
Jenkins, co., Ga., U.S.	D5	87
Jenkinsburg, Ga., U.S.	C2	87
Jenkinsville, S.C., U.S.	C5	117
Jenkintown, Pa., U.S.	o21	115
Jenks, Ok., U.S.	A6	113
Jenner, Ab., Can.	D5	68
Jenners, Pa., U.S.	F3	115
Jennie, Ar., U.S.	D4	81
Jennings, Fl., U.S.	B3	86
Jennings, Ks., U.S.	C3	93
Jennings, La., U.S.	D3	95
Jennings, Md., U.S.	k12	97
Jennings, Mi., U.S.	D5	99
Jennings, Mo., U.S.	f13	102
Jennings, Ok., U.S.	A5	113
Jennings, co., In., U.S.	G6	91
Jennings Lodge, Or., U.S.	*B4	114
Jenny Jump Mountain, mtn., N.J., U.S.	B3	107
Jenny Lind, Ar., U.S.	B1	81
Jensen, Ut., U.S.	C6	121
Jensen Beach, Fl., U.S.	E6	86
Jeptha Knob, hill, Ky., U.S.	B4	94
Jequitaí, Braz.	B4	56
Jequitinhonha, Braz.	B4	56
Jequitinhonha, stm., Braz.	E2	57
Jerada, Mor.	C4	44
Jerauld, co., S.D., U.S.	C7	118
Jérémie, Haiti	E6	64
Jeremoabo, Braz.	D3	57
Jerez de García Salinas, Mex.	C4	63
Jerez de la Frontera, Spain	D2	22
Jerez de los Caballeros, Spain	C2	22
Jericho, Austl.	A6	51
Jericho (Arīḥā), Isr. Occ.	C7	41
Jericho, Ar., U.S.	B5	81
Jericho, N.Y., U.S.	*E7	109
Jericho, Vt., U.S.	B3	122
Jericho Center, Vt., U.S.	C3	122
Jerico Springs, Mo., U.S.	D4	102
Jerimoth Hill, hill, R.I., U.S.	C1	116
Jermyn, Pa., U.S.	C10	115
Jermyn, Tx., U.S.	C3	120
Jerome, Az., U.S.	C3	80
Jerome, Ar., U.S.	D4	81
Jerome, Fl., U.S.	F5	86
Jerome, Id., U.S.	G4	89
Jerome, Ia., U.S.	D4	92
Jerome, Mi., U.S.	F6	99
Jerome, Mo., U.S.	D6	102
Jerome, Pa., U.S.	F4	115
Jerome, co., Id., U.S.	G4	89
Jeromesville, Oh., U.S.	B3	112
Jersey, Ga., U.S.	C3	87
Jersey, co., Il., U.S.	D3	90
Jersey, dep., Eur.	F5	10
Jersey City, N.J., U.S.	B4	107
Jersey Mountain, mtn., Id., U.S.	E3	89
Jersey Shore, Pa., U.S.	D7	115
Jerseyville, Il., U.S.	D3	90
Jerumenha, Braz.	C2	57
Jerusalem (Yerushalayim), Isr.	B3	38
Jerusalem, Ar., U.S.	B3	81
Jerusalem, Oh., U.S.	C4	112
Jervis Bay, b., Austl.	G9	50
Jervis Inlet, b., B.C., Can.	D6	69
Jesenice Reservoir, res., Czech.	C7	19
Jeseník, Czech.	C4	26
Jessamine, co., Ky., U.S.	C5	94
Jessen, Ger.D.R.	B7	19
Jessie, N.D., U.S.	B7	111
Jessieville, Ar., U.S.	C2	81
Jessnitz, Ger.D.R.	B7	19
Jessore, Bngl.	F12	37
Jessup, Md., U.S.	B4	97
Jessup, Pa., U.S.	m18	115
Jesterville, Md., U.S.	D6	97
Jesup, Ga., U.S.	E5	87
Jesup, Ia., U.S.	B5	92
Jesup, Lake, l., Fl., U.S.	D5	86
Jésus, Île, i., P.Q., Can.	p19	74
Jesús Carranza, Mex.	D5	63
Jesús María, Arg.	A4	54
Jesús María, Peru	*D2	58
Jet, Ok., U.S.	A3	113
Jetersville, Va., U.S.	C4	123
Jetmore, Ks., U.S.	D4	93
Jetson, Ky., U.S.	C3	94
Jette, Bel.	D4	17
Jeumont, Fr.	D4	17
Jever, F.R.Ger.	B3	18
Jewel Cave National Monument, S.D., U.S.	D2	118
Jewell, Ia., U.S.	B4	92
Jewell, Ks., U.S.	C5	93
Jewell, Oh., U.S.	A1	112
Jewell, co., Ks., U.S.	C5	93
Jewell Ridge, Va., U.S.	e10	123
Jewett, Il., U.S.	D5	90
Jewett, Oh., U.S.	B4	112
Jewett, Tx., U.S.	D4	120
Jewett City, Ct., U.S.	C8	84
Jewett Lake, l., Sk., Can.	A3	75
Jeypore, India	E7	36
Jeziorka, stm., Pol.	m14	26
Jhal, Pak.	C1	37
Jhālawār, India	E6	37
Jhal Jhao, Pak.	C4	36
Jhālrapātan, India	D6	36
Jhang Maghiāna, Pak.	B4	37
Jhang Sadar, Pak.	*B5	36
Jhānsi, India	C6	36
Jhawāni, Nepal	D10	37
Jhelum, Pak.	B5	36
Jhelum, stm., Asia	B5	36
Jhūnjhunu, India	C5	37
Jialing Jiang, stm., China	E6	31
Jiamusi, China	B11	31
Ji'an, China	F7	31
Ji'an, China	D12	32
Jianchang, China	D11	32
Jiande, China	J8	32
Jiangling, China	E7	31
Jiangmen, China	G7	31
Jiangsu, prov., China	E9	31
Jiangxi, prov., China	F8	31
Jiangyin (Chengjiang), China	I9	32
Jiangyou, China	E5	31
Jianli, China	J5	32
Jianning, China	K7	32
Jian'ou, China	F8	31
Jianping, China	C8	31
Jianshi, China	I3	32
Jianshui, China	G5	31
Jianyang, China	K8	32
Jiaohe, China	E3	33
Jiaoxian, China	D9	31
Jiaozhou Bay, b., China	F9	32
Jiaozuo, China	D7	31
Jiashan, China	H8	32
Jiaxian, China	E4	32
Jiaxing, China	E9	31
Jiayu, China	I5	32
Jicarilla Indian Reservation, N.M., U.S.	A2	108
Jičín, Czech.	C3	26
Jiddah, Sau. Ar.	C3	38
Jiddī, Jabal al, mtn., Eg.	D5	41
Jidy, Bi'r al, well, Eg.	D5	41
Jiek'kevarri, mtn., Nor.	C8	14
Jiexiu, China	F4	32
Jieyang, China	G8	31
Jifnā, Isr. Occ.	h11	41
Jigger, La., U.S.	B4	95
Jiggs, Nv., U.S.	C6	105
Jihlava, Czech.	D3	26
Jihočeský, prov., Czech.	D9	19
Jijel, Alg.	B6	44
Jijia, stm., Rom.	B8	24
Jijiga, Eth.	D5	47
Jijona, Spain	C5	22
Jilbānah, Bi'r al, well, Eg.	D4	41
Jilib, Som.	E5	47
Jilin, China	C10	31
Jilin, prov., China	C10	31
Jiloca, stm., Spain	B5	22
Jílové u Prahy, Czech.	o18	26
Jima, Eth.	D4	47
Jimbolia, Rom.	C5	24
Jimena [de los Frontera], Spain	D3	22
Jim Falls, Wi., U.S.	C2	126
Jim Hogg, co., Tx., U.S.	F3	120
Jim Lake, res., N.D., U.S.	B7	111
Jimo, China	F9	32
Jim Thorpe, Pa., U.S.	E10	115
Jim Wells, co., Tx., U.S.	F3	120
Jināḥ, Eg.	D6	43
Jinan (Tsinan), China	D8	31
Jincheng, China	G5	32
Jindřichův Hradec, Czech.	D3	26
Jingbian, China	F3	32
Jingchuan, China	G2	32
Jingde, China	I8	32
Jingdezhen, China	F8	31
Jing He, stm., China	G3	32
Jinghong, China	G5	31
Jingmen, China	I5	32
Jingning, China	G1	32
Jingshan, China	I5	32
Jingxi, China	D9	32
Jingxian, China	I8	32
Jingxian, China	K3	32
Jingxing, China	A10	32
Jingziguan, China	H4	32
Jinhua, China	F8	31
Jining, China	C7	31
Jining, China	D8	31
Jinja, Ug.	A5	48
Jinniu, China	I6	32
Jinotega, Nic.	E7	63
Jinotepe, Nic.	E7	63
Jinsha Jiang, stm., China	F4	31
Jinshi, China	J4	32
Jinta, China	C4	31
Jinxian, China	D9	31
Jinyun, China	J9	32
Jinzhou, China	C9	31
Ji-Paraná, Braz.	B3	55
Jiparaná, stm., Braz.	D2	59
Jipijapa, Ec.	B1	58
Jiquilisco, El Sal.	D3	62
Jiquilpan de Juárez, Mex.	n12	63
Jirjā, Eg.	C3	38
Jirkov, Czech.	C8	19
Jisr ash Shughūr, Syria	E11	40
Jiu, stm., Rom.	C6	24
Jiujiang, China	F8	31
Jiuquan, China	D4	31
Jiurongcheng, China	F10	32
Jīwani, Rās, c., Pak.	I10	39
Jixi, China	B11	31
Jixian, China	G6	32
Jizera, stm., Czech.	C9	19
Joaçaba, Braz.	D2	56
Joaíma, Braz.	B4	56
Joanna, S.C., U.S.	C4	117
João Belo see Xai-Xai, Moz.	C5	49
João Câmara, Braz.	g6	57
João Pessoa (Paraíba), Braz.	C4	57
João Pinheiro, Braz.	B3	56
Joaquín V. González, Arg.	E3	55
Job, W.V., U.S.	C5	125
Job Peak, mtn., Nv., U.S.	D3	105
Jobstown, N.J., U.S.	C3	107
Jocassee, Lake, res., U.S.	B1	117
Jocotepec, Mex.	m12	63
Jódar, Spain	D4	22
Jo Daviess, co., Il., U.S.	A3	90
Jodhpur, India	C5	36
Jodie, W.V., U.S.	m13	125
Jodoigne, Bel.	D4	17
Joe Batt's Arm, Nf., Can.	D4	72
Joensuu, Fin.	F13	14
Joes, Co., U.S.	B8	83
Joes Brook, stm., Vt., U.S.	C4	122
Joes Creek, stm., W.V., U.S.	m12	125
Joetsu, Japan	H9	33
Jœuf, Fr.	C6	16
Joffre, Mount, mtn., Can.	D3	68
Joggins, N.S., Can.	D5	71
Jogjakarta see Yogyakarta, Indon.	G4	34
Johannesburg, S. Afr.	C4	49
Johannesburg, Ca., U.S.	E5	82
Johannesburg, Mi., U.S.	D6	99
John, Cape, c., N.S., Can.	D6	71
John Crow Mountains, mts., Jam.	E16	65
John Day, Or., U.S.	C8	114
John Day, stm., Or., U.S.	B6	114
John Day, North Fork, stm., Or., U.S.	C7	114
John Day Dam, U.S.	D5	124
John Day Fossil Beds National Monument, Or., U.S.	C6	114
John F. Kennedy Space Center, sci., Fl., U.S.	D6	86
John H. Kerr Dam, Va., U.S.	D4	123
John H. Kerr Reservoir, res., U.S.	D4	123
John Martin Reservoir, res., Co., U.S.	C7	83
John Muir National Historical Site, hist., Ca., U.S.	h8	82
John o'Groats, Scot., U.K.	B5	13
John Redmond Reservoir, res., Ks., U.S.	D8	93
Johnsburg, Il., U.S.	h8	90
Johnsburg, N.Y., U.S.	B7	109
Johnsburg, Wi., U.S.	k9	126
John Sevier, Tn., U.S.	m14	119
Johns Island, S.C., U.S.	F7	117
Johns Island, i., S.C., U.S.	F7	117
Johnson, Ar., U.S.	A1	81
Johnson, In., U.S.	H2	91
Johnson, Ks., U.S.	E2	93
Johnson, Ne., U.S.	D10	104
Johnson, Vt., U.S.	B3	122
Johnson, Wa., U.S.	C8	124
Johnson, co., Ar., U.S.	B2	81
Johnson, co., Ga., U.S.	D4	87
Johnson, co., Il., U.S.	F5	90
Johnson, co., In., U.S.	F5	91
Johnson, co., Ia., U.S.	C6	92
Johnson, co., Ks., U.S.	D9	93
Johnson, co., Ky., U.S.	C7	94
Johnson, co., Mo., U.S.	C4	102
Johnson, co., Ne., U.S.	D9	104
Johnson, co., Tn., U.S.	C12	119
Johnson, co., Tx., U.S.	C4	120
Johnson, co., Wy., U.S.	B6	127
Johnsonburg, Pa., U.S.	D4	115
Johnson City, N.Y., U.S.	C5	109
Johnson City, Tn., U.S.	C11	119
Johnson City, Tx., U.S.	D3	120
Johnson Creek, Wi., U.S.	E5	126
Johnsondale, Ca., U.S.	E4	82
Johnson's Bayou, La., U.S.	E2	95
Johnsons Grove, Tn., U.S.	B2	119
Johnsonville, S.C., U.S.	D9	117
Johns Pass, strt., Fl., U.S.	p10	86
Johnston, Ia., U.S.	e8	92
Johnston, R.I., U.S.	C4	116
Johnston, S.C., U.S.	D4	117
Johnston, co., N.C., U.S.	B4	110
Johnston, co., Ok., U.S.	C5	113
Johnston, i., Oc.	E11	6
Johnston, Lake, l., Austl.	F3	50
Johnston City, Il., U.S.	F5	90
Johnstone, Scot., U.K.	*E4	13
Johnstone Strait, strt., B.C., Can.	D4	69
Johnston Key, i., Fl., U.S.	H5	86
Johnston's Point, c., Scot., U.K.	E3	13
Johnstown, Co., U.S.	A6	83
Johnstown, Ne., U.S.	B5	104
Johnstown, N.Y., U.S.	B6	109
Johnstown, N.D., U.S.	A8	111
Johnstown, Oh., U.S.	B3	112
Johnstown, Pa., U.S.	F4	115
Johnsville, Md., U.S.	A3	97
Johntown, Tx., U.S.	C5	120
Johnville, P.Q., Can.	D6	74
John W. Flannagan Reservoir, res., Va., U.S.	e9	123
Johor, state, Malay.	K5	35
Johor Baharu, Malay.	E2	34
Joice, Ia., U.S.	A4	92
Joigny, Fr.	D5	16
Joiner, Ar., U.S.	B5	81
Joinvile, Braz.	D3	56
Joinville, Fr.	C6	16
Joinville Island, i., Ant.	C7	7
Jojutla, Mex.	n14	63
Jokkmokk, Swe.	D8	14
Jolfā, Iran	B2	39
Joliet, Il., U.S.	B5	90
Joliet, Mt., U.S.	E8	103
Joliette, P.Q., Can.	C4	74
Joliette, N.D., U.S.	A8	111
Joliette, co., P.Q., Can.	C3	74
Jolley, Ia., U.S.	B3	92
Jolo, Phil.	D6	34
Jomalig Island, i., Phil.	o14	34
Jomda, China	E4	31
Jonas Ridge, N.C., U.S.	B1	110
Jonava, Sov. Un.	A8	26
Jones, Phil.	n13	34
Jones, Al., U.S.	C3	78
Jones, Ga., U.S.	E5	87
Jones, La., U.S.	B4	95
Jones, Ok., U.S.	B4	113
Jones, co., Ga., U.S.	C3	87
Jones, co., Ia., U.S.	B6	92
Jones, co., Ms., U.S.	D4	101
Jones, co., N.C., U.S.	B5	110
Jones, co., S.D., U.S.	D5	118
Jones, co., Tx., U.S.	C3	120
Jonesboro, Ar., U.S.	B5	81
Jonesboro, Ga., U.S.	C2	87
Jonesboro, Il., U.S.	F4	90
Jonesboro, In., U.S.	D6	91
Jonesboro, La., U.S.	B3	95
Jonesboro, Me., U.S.	D5	96
Jonesboro, Tn., U.S.	C11	119
Jonesboro, Tx., U.S.	D4	120
Jonesburg, Mo., U.S.	C6	102
Jones Creek, Tx., U.S.	s14	120
Jones Mill, Ar., U.S.	C3	81
Jones Mill, Tn., U.S.	A3	119
Jones Mills, Pa., U.S.	F3	115
Jones Mountains, mts., Ant.	B3	7
Jonesport, Me., U.S.	D5	96
Jones Sound, strt., N.T., Can.	m34	66
Jonestown, Ms., U.S.	C3	101
Jonestown, Ms., U.S.	A3	101
Jonestown, Pa., U.S.	F9	115
Jonesville, In., U.S.	F6	91
Jonesville, La., U.S.	C4	95
Jonesville, Mi., U.S.	G6	99
Jonesville, N.C., U.S.	A2	110
Jonesville, S.C., U.S.	B4	117
Jonesville, Vt., U.S.	C3	122
Jonesville, Va., U.S.	f8	123
Jönköping, Swe.	I6	14
Jönköping, co., Swe.	A8	15
Jonquière, P.Q., Can.	A6	74
Jonuta, Mex.	D6	63
Jonzac, Fr.	E3	16
Joplin, Mo., U.S.	D3	102
Joplin, Mt., U.S.	B6	103
Joppa, Al., U.S.	A3	78
Joppa, Il., U.S.	F5	90
Joppa, Md., U.S.	B5	97
Jordan, Al., U.S.	D1	78
Jordan, Ar., U.S.	A3	81
Jordan, Ky., U.S.	f8	94
Jordan, Mn., U.S.	F5	100
Jordan, Mt., U.S.	C10	103
Jordan, N.Y., U.S.	B4	109
Jordan, ctry., Asia	B3	38
Jordan, stm., Asia	B7	41
Jordan, stm., Ut., U.S.	C4	121
Jordan Creek, stm., U.S.	E9	114
Jordan Lake, l., N.S., Can.	E4	71
Jordan Lake, res., Al., U.S.	C3	78
Jordan Valley, Or., U.S.	D9	114
Jorhāt, India	C9	36
Jörn, Swe.	E9	14
Jornado del Muerto, des., N.M., U.S.	D3	108
Jos, Nig.	E6	45
José Batlle y Ordóñez, Ur.	E1	56
José de San Martín, Arg.	C2	54
José María Blanco, Arg.	B4	54
Joseph, Or., U.S.	B9	114
Joseph, Ut., U.S.	E3	121
Joseph, Lac, l., Nf., Can.	h8	72
Joseph, Lake, l., On., Can.	B5	73
Joseph Bonaparte Gulf, b., Austl.	B4	50
Joseph City, Az., U.S.	C5	80
Josephine, co., Or., U.S.	E3	114
Josephville, Mo., U.S.	f12	102
Joshua, Tx., U.S.	n9	120
Joshua Tree, Ca., U.S.	E5	82
Joshua Tree National Monument, Ca., U.S.	F6	82
Josselin, Fr.	C2	16
Jostedalsbreen, Nor.	G2	14
Jost Van Dyke, i., V.I., Br.	B6	65
Jotunheimen, mts., Nor.	G3	14
Jourdanton, Tx., U.S.	E3	120
Joussard, Ab., Can.	B3	68
Joux, Lake, l., Switz.	C2	20
Jouy-en-Josas, Fr.	g9	16
Jovellanos, Cuba	C3	64
Joveyn, Afg.	B3	36
Joviânia, Braz.	B3	56
Jowhar, Som.	E6	47
Joy, Il., U.S.	B3	90
Joy, Ok., U.S.	C4	113
Joyce, La., U.S.	C3	95
Joyce, Wa., U.S.	A2	124
Józefów, Pol.	m14	26
J. Percy Priest Lake, res., Tn., U.S.	A5	119
Juab, co., Ut., U.S.	D2	121
Juaja, Peru	D2	58
Juan Aldama, Mex.	C4	63
Juan B. Arruabarrena, Arg.	A5	54
Juan de Fuca, Strait of, strt., N.A.	A1	124
Juan Díaz (part of Panamá), Pan.	k12	62
Juan E. Barra, Arg.	B4	54
Juan Fernández, Archipiélago, is., Chile	G2	53
Juanita, N.D., U.S.	B7	111
Juan José Castelli, Arg.	E3	55
Juanjuí, Peru	C2	58
Juan L. Lacaze, Ur.	g8	54
Juárez, Mex.	B4	63
Juaso, Ghana	E4	45
Juazeiro, Braz.	C2	57
Juazeiro do Norte, Braz.	C3	57
Jūbā, Sud.	E3	47
Jubba (Genale), stm., Afr.	E5	47
Jubbada Dhexe, prov., Som.	E5	47
Jubbada Hoose, prov., Som.	E5	47
Jubbah, Sau. Ar.	I13	40
Jubilee Lake, l., Nf., Can.	D4	72
Juby, Cap, c., Mor.	D2	44
Júcar, stm., Spain	C5	22
Juçara, Braz.	B2	56
Júcaro, Cuba	D4	64
Juchipila, Mex.	m12	63
Juchipila, stm., Mex.	m12	63
Juchitán [de Zaragoza], Mex.	D5	63
Jucuapa, El Sal.	D3	62
Jud, N.D., U.S.	C7	111
Juda, Wi., U.S.	F4	126
Judayyidat 56 Ar56 ar, Sau. Ar.	G13	40
Judean Hills, hills, Asia	C7	41
Jude Island, i., Nf., Can.	E4	72
Judenburg, Aus.	E7	18
Judique, N.S., Can.	D8	71
Judith, stm., Mt., U.S.	C7	103
Judith, Point, c., R.I., U.S.	G4	85
Judith Basin, co., Mt., U.S.	C6	103
Judith Gap, Mt., U.S.	D7	103
Judith Island, i., N.C., U.S.	B6	110
Judith Mountains, mts., Mt., U.S.	C7	103
Judith Peak, mtn., Mt., U.S.	C7	103
Judson, In., U.S.	E3	91
Judson, Mn., U.S.	F4	100
Judson, N.D., U.S.	C4	111
Judsonia, Ar., U.S.	B4	81
Judyville, In., U.S.	D3	91
Juelsminde, Den.	C4	15
Jufayr, Bi'r al, well, Eg.	D4	41
Juigalpa, Nic.	D5	62
Juist, F.R.Ger.	A6	17
Juist, i., F.R.Ger.	B3	18
Juiz de Fora, Braz.	C4	56
Jujuy, prov., Arg.	D2	55
Jukkasjärvi (part of Kiruna), Swe.	D9	14
Julesburg, Co., U.S.	A8	83
Juliaca, Peru	E3	58
Juliaetta, Id., U.S.	C2	89
Julian, Ca., U.S.	F5	82
Julian, Ne., U.S.	D10	104
Julian, N.C., U.S.	B3	110
Julian, W.V., U.S.	C3	125
Julian Alps, mts., Eur.	C2	24
Juliana Top, mtn., Sur.	B3	59
Julianehåb, Grnld.	C16	61
Jülich, F.R.Ger.	D6	17
Juliette, Ga., U.S.	C3	87
Julimes, Mex.	B3	63
Júlio de Castilhos, Braz.	D2	56
Julita, Swe.	t34	14
Juliustown, N.J., U.S.	C3	107
Jullundur, India	B6	36
Julu, China	F6	32
Jumayl, Bi'r, well, Eg.	D5	41
Jumboo, Som.	F5	47
Jumbo Peak, mtn., Nv., U.S.	G7	105
Jumet (part of Charleroi), Bel.	B6	16
Jumilla, Spain	C5	22
Jump, stm., Wi., U.S.	C3	126
Jump, North Fork, stm., Wi., U.S.	C3	126
Jump, South Fork, stm., Wi., U.S.	C3	126
Jumping Branch, W.V., U.S.	D4	125
Jumping Lake, l., Sk., Can.	E3	75
Junāgadh, India	D5	36
Juncos, P.R.	B4	65
Junction, Il., U.S.	F5	90
Junction, Oh., U.S.	A1	112
Junction, Tx., U.S.	D3	120
Junction, Ut., U.S.	E3	121
Junction City, Ar., U.S.	D3	81
Junction City, Ga., U.S.	D2	87
Junction City, Il., U.S.	E4	90
Junction City, Ks., U.S.	C7	93
Junction City, Ky., U.S.	C5	94
Junction City, La., U.S.	A3	95
Junction City, Oh., U.S.	C3	112
Junction City, Or., U.S.	C3	114
Junction City, Wi., U.S.	D4	126
Jundiaí, Braz.	C3	56
Juneau, Ak., U.S.	D13	79
Juneau, Wi., U.S.	E5	126
Juneau, co., Wi., U.S.	E3	126
Junee, Austl.	F8	50
June in Winter, Lake, l., Fl., U.S.	E5	86
June Lake, Ca., U.S.	D4	82
Jungfrau, mtn., Switz.	E3	18
Junglinster, Lux.	E6	17
Juniata, Ne., U.S.	D7	104
Juniata, co., Pa., U.S.	F7	115
Juniata, stm., Pa., U.S.	F7	115
Juniata, Raystown Branch, stm., Pa., U.S.	F5	115
Juniata Terrace, Pa., U.S.	E6	115
Junín, Arg.	A4	54
Junín, Peru	D2	58
Junín, dept., Peru	D2	58
Junín, Lago, l., Peru	D2	58
Junín de los Andes, Arg.	B2	54
Junior, W.V., U.S.	C5	125
Junior Lake, l., Me., U.S.	C4	96
Juniper, N.B., Can.	C2	71
Juniper Mountains, mts., Az., U.S.	B2	80
Junipero Serra Peak, mtn., Ca., U.S.	D3	82
Junius, S.D., U.S.	C8	118
Juno, Tx., U.S.	D2	120
Junqalī, prov., Sud.	D3	47
Juntura, Or., U.S.	D8	114
Jupiter, Fl., U.S.	F6	86
Jupiter Inlet, b., Fl., U.S.	F6	86
Jupiter Island, i., Fl., U.S.	E6	86
Juquiá, Braz.	C3	56
Juquitiba, Braz.	m8	56
Jura, state, Switz.	B3	20
Jura, dept., Fr.	C1	20
Jura, i., Scot., U.K.	C4	10
Jura, Sound of, strt., Scot., U.K.	C4	10
Jura Mountains, mts., Eur.	E3	18
Jurbarkas, Sov. Un.	A7	26
Jurf ad Darāwīsh, Jord.	G10	40
Juruá, Braz.	B4	58
Juruá, stm., S.A.	B4	58
Juruena, stm., Braz.	D3	59
Juruti, Braz.	C3	59
Juskatla, B.C., Can.	C1	69
Jussey, Fr.	B1	20
Justice, Il., U.S.	*k9	90
Justiceburg, Tx., U.S.	C2	120
Justin, Tx., U.S.	C4	120
Justo Daract, Arg.	A3	54
Jutaí, Braz.	C4	58
Jutaí, stm., Braz.	B4	58
Jüterbog, Ger.D.R.	C6	18
Jutiapa, Guat.	E7	63
Juticalpa, Hond.	E7	63
Jutland, pen., Den.	I3	14
Juventud, Isla de la (Isle of Pines), i., Cuba	D2	64
Juxian, China	G8	32
Juyongguan Pass, China	D7	32
Južna Morava, stm., Yugo.	D5	24
Jyderup, Den.	C5	15
Jyväskylä, Fin.	F11	14

K

Name	Map Ref	Page
K2 (Godwin Austen), mtn., Asia	A6	36
Kaaawa, Hi., U.S.	f10	88
Kaala, mtn., Hi., U.S.	f9	88
Kaalualu Bay, b., Hi., U.S.	E6	88
Kaaumakua, Puu, mtn., Hi., U.S.	f10	88
Kabala, S.L.	E2	45
Kabale, Ug.	B4	48
Kabalega Falls (Murchison Falls), wtfl, Ug.	A5	48
Kabalo, Zaire	C4	48
Kabambare, Zaire	B4	48
Kabara, i., Fiji	I16	52
Kabarnet, Kenya	A6	48
Kabba, Nig.	E6	45
Kabenga, Zaire	C4	48
Kabetogama Lake, l., Mn., U.S.	B5	100
Kabinda, Zaire	C3	48
Kabīr Kūh, mts., Iran	E3	39
Kabompo, Zam.	D3	48
Kabompo, stm., Zam.	D3	48
Kabong, Malay.	E4	34
Kabongo, Zaire	C4	48
Kabul, Afg.	B4	36
Kabul, stm., Asia	D14	39
Kabwe (Broken Hill), Zam.	D4	48
Kachess Lake, res., Wa., U.S.	B4	124
Kachug, Sov. Un.	D13	29
Kackley, Ks., U.S.	C6	93
Kadaň, Czech.	C2	26
Kadan, i., Burma	F3	35
Kadavu, i., Fiji	I15	52
Kade, Ghana	E4	45

Index

Name	Map Ref	Page

Index

Index

Swan-Tata

Name	Map Ref	Page

V

Name	Map Ref	Page

Index

Name	Map Ref	Page

222

Yuci-Zywi

Index